GW00357619

The
GOLFERS
ALMANAC

Malcolm Campbell

LOCHAR PUBLISHING•MOFFAT•SCOTLAND

For Sandra, Dugald and Isi

© Malcolm Campbell, 1991
Published by Lochar Publishing Ltd
MOFFAT DG10 9ED

British Library Cataloguing in Publication Data
Campbell, Malcolm
The Golfers almanac.
1. Golfers 2. Great Britain and Ireland
I. Title
796.35206841

ISBN 0-948403-84-5

Typeset in 8 on 8½pt Triumvirate by
Chapterhouse, Formby, L37 3PX
and printed in Scotland by Eagle Colourbooks

Publisher's Note
All information given in the following pages was
correct at the time of printing.

Acknowledgements
There are many who have given me valuable assistance
in the compilation of this book but I would like to extend a
particular vote of thanks to several people. To the
secretaries of the clubs highlighted in the book I extend a
special thanks for their considerable help. Golf club
secretaries are busy people whose contribution to the
game goes largely unsung and I thank them for granting
me so much of their valuable time. I am extremely
grateful to David Duckering at Strokesport for his help
with the photographic content. Last but not least a
particular thank you to my wife, Sandra, for the many
hours she contributed to the processing of information
and typing the manuscript.

CONTENTS

FOREWORD

Golf to most of us is a way of life and we pass along its sometimes tortuous but more often humorous and enjoyable path alas but once. I commend this volume to you as a worthy companion along the way for in it you will find a wonderful selection of courses for the journey.

Within these covers is a grand tour not only of the great championship links of the British Isles but many of the lesser-known gems which are easily missed unless they are brought to your attention.

It is a well balanced selection which I believe fulfills entirely the aim of highlighting courses which have more to offer than just reputation or challenge.

There is very little point in recommending a course to someone if they cannot normally go there and be able to play. All the courses in the "Golfers Almanac" welcome visitors – some with more restrictions than others but that is the nature of things – and within its covers is a selection that will appeal to the widest possible taste.

The author, in the course of many years as a highly regarded and widely travelled golf writer, has visited and played hundreds of courses in Britain and around the world and is well qualified to make the selection.

Many of the courses bring back fond memories to me and I hope you enjoy it as much as I have.

Tony Jacklin

INTRODUCTION

There are few in this golfing life who do not relish the opportunity to seek the challenge of another golf course away from their native heath. The glorious truth is that there are so many to choose from and the tragedy that one lifetime is so far from being enough to sample even the very best of them.

I have been blessed with great fortune in that I have been able to visit and play so many all over the world in the course of ten years as Editor of Golf Monthly and to find so many new golfing friends along the way.

Golf is now in the middle of its second great boom. In the 1880s the first golf boom took the game from being a relatively obscure obsession of the Scots, confined mainly to their ancient kingdom, to a game which swept to popularity in all parts of the civilised world – and indeed in some parts which were not civilised at all. It was inevitable of course that the Scots would be the great missionaries. They not only took the game with them to far flung outposts of expanding empire they took with it the knowledge of how to make the equipment and, just as importantly, how to create the courses upon which this game of club and ball was played.

They had long experience of it for no matter how some eminent men may argue the finer points of the origins of the game there is no doubt that the game as we know it today developed in Scotland, and has been played for centuries.

Club and ball games can be traced as far back as the Romans who indulged in Paganica, a game played, legend has it, with a bent stick and a ball made from leather stuffed with feathers. But all the evidence points to the fact that it was the Scots who introduced the one element which makes golf different from all other club and ball games – the hole.

Various learned and distinguished souls have presented the case variously for the Romans, the French and Dutch as the first players of "the gowf" but the various forms of club and ball pastime which they offer as evidence lack the vital requirement for the ball to finish beneath the surface of the earth. Golf is truly the game with the hole in it.

It is the only game in which the ball begins its journey in mid air, poised on a tiny piece of scaffolding, and completes the trip underground. All other historic club and ball games brought in evidence to support the lobby which would take the origins of golf away from Scotland are but imposters.

The royal and ancient game as we know it today is a Caledonian product pure and simple and the great courses on which it is played, if they have not actually been built by the Scots, have been almost totally influenced by them.

The history of golf and its courses is really the history of the modern game as we know it today going back a little over a century to the time of the introduction of the gutta percha ball which superseded the crude and expensive feathery ball in the mid-1880's and brought the game within the reach of the masses.

The feather ball, made from a top hat full of boiled goose feathers and stuffed at great personal hardship into small leather pouches by the first golf professionals, was not only expensive to manufacture it was extremely inefficient and prone to easy damage.

The gutta percha ball revolutionised the game and the clubs with which it was played. The tough new material was resistant to impact with iron headed clubs in a way that the feathery was not and so a whole new range of golfing implements was born.

But the most significant aspect of the arrival of the gutta perch ball was that fact that it made golf more accessible to the population and fuelled that first great golf boom in the latter part of the 19th century.

The demand for the game brought with it the necessity to build more courses and the great golf course building boom of mid-Victorian times is reflected in the huge number of golf clubs which are now, or have been in recent years, celebrating centenaries.

If, as has so often been claimed, nature was the first golf course architect with the Old Course at St Andrews the classic example then the Scots were the natural successors. Legendary figures like Old Tom Morris, who would build anyone a course for £1 a day plus his expenses, and Willie Park and James Braid among many prolific builders, set the standards. Others left their native land to build courses all over the world and nowhere more obviously than the United States where a thousand golf courses were build in the last decade of the 19th century. Others, still like Alister Mackenzie who designed Augusta National with Bobby Jones and Donald Ross who built Pinehurst, came later and refined the golf course architect's art maintaining at the same time the Scottish influence.

There are few modern course architects who are not influenced by these great pioneers, one very good reason why the world is so well appointed in terms of marvellous places to pursue the royal and ancient game.

Scotland is accepted the world over as the home of the game but the British Isles as a whole has a supply of magnificent golf courses which is the envy of the golfing world.

What I set out to do in the Golfer's Almanac was assemble in one handy-sized volume a selection of courses throughout the British Isles to reflect the widest possible variety from the great championship links to the hidden golfing gems off the beaten track. But more important than that was to list clubs which would genuinely welcome serious and responsible visitors to their courses.

My criterion for including a course in this list of just over a hundred was not simply that it was a great challenge or that it had hosted a major championship or event. This is not, therefore, a list of the "best" or "top 100" courses in the British Isles; to have attempted that would have been an act of supreme subjective arrogance. Rather, it is an assembly of courses which offer challenge and good facilities of scenic splendour in varying degrees but which all have one thing in common – the warmth of welcome to the visitor.

At a time when courses have never been busier trying to cope with the demand of the new golf boom I have tried to include lesser-known courses where perhaps there is less pressure as well as several of the great championship links which have hosted the Open, for instance, and others still which are tucked away in relative obscurity but which are well worth rooting out.

Hopefully the reader will find something to suit his taste or mood and can plan a visit in the knowledge that the information which each entry contains is the very latest available at the time of going to press and provided specifically by each club.

Where certain clubs on my original list have been approached and have indicated a less than enthusiastic welcome to visitors, which of course is their prerogative, they have simply been left out for they have no place in this volume.

It is pleasing to report that such clubs have been few and far between and safe to say that they will hardly be missed.

The vast majority on the other hand could not have been more helpful in providing the information which will help the prospective visitor and my sincerest thanks go to hard-worked secretaries all over the British Isles who have taken the time and effort to assist me in the research.

My earnest hope is that the Golfers Almanac will be an accurate and valuable aid to serious and responsible golfers who wish to enjoy fine facilities at courses and clubs where they know they will find a warm welcome.

It must be emphasised that my list has been restricted to around a hundred quite simply through constraints on space and is in no way a suggestion that these are the only clubs which welcome visitors. This is far from the case. There are many hundreds of courses which welcome visitors enthusiastically and provide equal challenge and facilities. The Golfers Almanac is simply a tour of my pesonal selection built up over many years and I hope it will help others to look to new horizons and for new courses to conquer in this great game we all love so much.

Each course is listed with a brief description and information on such things as club contact names and telephone numbers, how to arrange tee times, restrictions on starting times, green fees, catering facilities, provision for club and caddie hire and other useful information for the visitor.

If there is one plea I have to make it is that those who visit the clubs listed in the Golfer s Almanac respect the rules and standards of their hosts. It is a plea which perhaps a few years ago, before the great golf explosion, might not need to have been made but it must never be overlooked that visitors to golf clubs are invited guests and we all owe a duty to the integrity of the game to remember that.

For those who manage to visit some of the courses I hope you enjoy them as much as I have in putting the Golfers Almanac together.

Malcolm Campbell
Auchinloch
Scotland 1991

SCOTLAND

The origins of golf in Scotland are lost in the mists of antiquity but it is certain that the game has been played there for centuries. It is thought to have been played as much as a century before James II, in an Act of Parliament of 1457, ordered that "golfe be utterly cryed downe".

That the Scots took little notice there is ample evidence for there were at least two more similar edicts intended to concentrate the minds of subjects on archery, jousting and allied martial activities rather than golf.

Defence of the Scottish realm was at stake and there were severe penalties for those who disobeyed. It is not hard with the benefit of hindsight to understand the monarch's concern for less than fifty years later the Scots were no match for the English archers and they suffered ignominious defeat and the loss of their king and the flower of their noble families at the Battle of Flodden Field in 1513.

During the sixteenth century golf became firmly established on the east coast and began to spread further afield. James VI became a convert before he acceded to the English throne as James I in 1603 and his mother, Mary Queen of Scots, was also a notable player. Indeed so keen was she that she fell foul of the Church for playing golf only a few days after the murder of her husband, Lord Darnley, in 1567.

The royal connection with the game helped spread it across Scotland. By the start of the seventeenth century it was being played from Orkney to the south-east corner of the country but it would be another 150 years before there was any move to bring organization to the game.

The humps and hollows of the linksland stretching for miles along the east coast were perfect for playing golf with their fine grasses cropped by grazing rabbits and sheep.

It was in these surroundings that the game took shape and developed and the standards and rules were established.

Today the most famous course of them all, the Old Course at St Andrews, stands testimony to those ancient times for golf is known to have been played there for five hundred years.

Today there are more than 400 courses in Scotland for the visitor to choose from and among them are many survivors of the very earliest days of the game.

ALYTH GOLF CLUB
Pitcrocknie, Alyth

James Braid designed this fine but less widely known course situated sixteen miles from Dundee. It is a heathland layout with some fine holes and panoramic views of the Perthshire countryside. Length is not the dominating factor. At just over 6200 yards it is a comfortable journey round but it provides challenge enough and is excellent holiday golf.

Secretary:	Mr. H. Sullivan Tel. 08282 2268
Professional:	Tommy Melville
	Tel. 08283 2411
Holes:	18
Length:	6226 yards.
	Par: 70 SSS: 70
Visitors:	Alyth Golf Club welcomes visitors without restriction.
Ladies & Juniors:	As for men.
Parties:	Parties are welcome except at weekends by prior arrangement with the Secretary – Tel. 08283 2268.
Green Fees:	Men & Ladies £18.50 per round; £23.50 per day. Junior £2 per round; £3 per day.
Club Hire:	Club hire can be arranged.
Caddies:	There are no caddies available. Caddy cars and electric trollies are available for hire.
Practice Ground:	The Club has practice facilities.
Catering:	The Clubhouse offers full catering facilities from 9am to 9pm.
Tee Times:	By arrangement with the Professional or his Assistant – Tel. 08283 2411.
Handicap:	A handicap certificate is not required.
Handicap Limit:	There is no handicap limit.

BANCHORY GOLF CLUB
(ESTABLISHED 1905)
Kinneskie Road, Banchory, AB31 3TA

Set among the splendour of Royal Deeside, Banchory is an inland course combining open parkland with tree-lined fairways. Length is not the challenge on this course perfect for holiday golf but the par 3's are long and challenging. The 11th, which is 180 yards long with out-of-bounds on the left and a burn in front of the green, is widely regarded as the best of them. The course runs alongside the River Dee.

Secretary:	Mr. E. Girvan Tel. 03302 2365
Professional:	Douglas Smart Tel. 03302 2447
Holes:	18
Length:	5245 yards. Par: 67 SSS: 66
Visitors:	Visitors are welcome with no restrictions other than reasonable competence.
Ladies & Juniors:	No restrictions other than as above.
Parties:	Parties are welcome by arrangement with the club secretary but restricted to Monday to Friday bookings.
Green Fees:	Men & Ladies £15 per day; £48 per week. Juniors £7.50 per day.
Club Hire:	Club hire is available from the professional's shop.
Caddies:	Caddies are not available.
Practice Ground:	The Club has a short practice ground.
Catering:	The club offers full catering facilities without restrictions. Contact – Tel. 03302 2365.
Tee Times:	By arrangement with the Club Professional – Tel. 03302 2447.
Handicap:	Handicap certificates are not required.
Handicap Limit:	Men 28; Ladies 36; Juniors 28.

BLAIRGOWRIE GOLF CLUB
(ESTABLISHED 1889)
Golf Course Road, Rosemount, Blairgowrie

The famous Blairgowrie Club, more widely known as Rosemount, has some of the finest inland golf in the British Isles. Set in heavily wooded countryside, the two courses represent a significant contrast. The original Rosemount course is a serene but demanding layout which underwent some changes to accommodate the new Landsdowne course, a product of the design team of Peter Alliss and Dave Thomas. The latter is a modern layout owing much to American thinking but a perfect foil for the Old course where Greg Norman won his first European event in 1977.

Secretary:	Mr. J. N. Simpson Tel. 0250 2622
Professional:	Gordon Kinnoch Tel. 0250 2622
Holes:	18
Length:	Old Course 6588 yards.
	Par: 72 SSS: 72
Visitors:	Blairgowrie Golf Club welcomes visitors except on Wednesdays and Fridays and at Weekends.
Ladies & Juniors:	As for men.
Parties:	Parties are welcome on Mondays, Tuesdays and Thursdays by arrangement with the Secretary – Tel. 0250 2622.
Green Fees:	Men & Ladies and Juniors £20 per round £30 per day £120 per week.
Club Hire:	Club hire can be arranged.
Caddies:	Caddies are available by arrangement. Caddy cars, electric trollies and buggies are available for hire.
Practice Ground:	The Club has both a full length and a short practice ground.
Catering:	The Clubhouse offers full catering facilities.
Tee Times:	Contact the Starter – Tel. 0250 2594.
Handicap:	An official handicap certificate is required.
Handicap Limit:	Men 28; Ladies 36; Juniors 36.

Blairgowrie Golf Club

BELLEISLE GOLF CLUB
(ESTABLISHED 1927)
Belleisle, Ayr, Scotland

The Belleisle course lies in a splendid parkland setting amid the splendour of Burns Country. James Braid designed the original course and today it is widely regarded as one of the best public gold courses in the British Isles. The course is home to the popular Ayr Golf Week, has been the venue for several professional events and is an excellent challenge.

Starter:	Tel. 0292 41258
	Fax. 2092 267813
Professional:	David Gemmell
	Tel. 0292 41314
Holes:	18
Length:	6477 yards.
	Par: 71 SSS: 71
Visitors:	Belleisle Golf Club welcomes visitors.
Ladies & Juniors:	There is no restriction on Ladies. Juniors must be 16 years of age, have a handicap of 12 or better and are restricted to play before 5.30pm Mon/Fri and after 3pm Sat. There is no Sunday play for juniors.
Parties:	The Club welcomes parties by arrangement with the course starter. Contact – Tel. 2092 41258.
Green Fees:	Men & Ladies £10.20 per round. Juniors £5.10 per round.
Club Hire:	By arrangement.
Caddies:	Caddies are not available.
Practice Ground:	There is a full length practice ground.
Catering:	Full catering facilities are available.
Tee Times:	Tee times by arrangement with the Starter Contact Ayr Tel. 41258.
Handicap:	No handicap certificate required.
Handicap Limit:	Men and Ladies – none. Juniors – 12.

Belleisle Golf Club

BOAT OF GARTEN GOLF CLUB
(ESTABLISHED 1898)
Boat of Garten, Inverness-shire, PH24 3BQ

One of Scotland's most picturesque golf courses Boat of Garten lies in the shadow of the Cairngorms not far from the ski centre of Aviemore. The James Braid layout is not long by modern standards but it presents a stern enough test for anyone, with the 6th hole regarded as one of the best in Scotland. A wide variety of wildlife, including deer and the rare osprey, are often seen from the course.

Secretary:	Mr. J. R. Ingram Tel. 0479 983 282
Professional:	None.
Holes:	18
Length:	5765 yards.
	Par: 69 SSS: 68
Visitors:	Boat of Garten Golf Club welcomes visitors without restriction.
Ladies & Juniors:	No restrictions.
Parties:	Parties are welcome by arrangement with the Club Secretary. Contact – Tel. 047 933 282.
Green Fees:	Men & Ladies £12 per day; £15 weekends; £60 per week. Juniors under 16 yeas of age £6 per day; £25 per week.
Club Hire:	Clubs are not available for hire.
Caddies:	Caddies, caddy cars and buggies are available.
Practice Ground:	The Club does not have a practice ground.
Catering:	Full catering facilities are available between 10am and 6pm or later by arrangement.
Tee Times:	Contact the Secretary – Tel. 047 983 282.
Handicap:	A handicap certificate is required.
Handicap Limit:	Men 28; Ladies 36; Juniors 36.

BUCKPOOL GOLF CLUB
Barhill Road, Buckie, Banffshire, AB56 1DJ

Wide fairways and well-groomed greens are a feature of this fine Banffshire course which is ideal for holiday golf. There are fine views to Spey Bay and Lossiemouth from fairways lined with whin and broom. The club has an enviable reputation for fine hospitality. It also has its own sports hall with badminton or carpet-bowling, two squash courts and a full-size snooker table. There is a separate lounge for juniors.

Secretary:	Mrs. I. E. Jagger Tel. 0542 32236
Professional:	No resident professional.
Holes:	18
Length:	6257 yards.
	Par: 70 SSS: 70
Visitors:	Buckpool Golf Club welcomes visitors without restriction by arrangement with the Secretary. Contact – Tel. 0542 32236.
Ladies & Juniors:	No restrictions.
Parties:	Parties are welcome by arrangement with the Secretary – Tel. 0542 32236
Green Fees:	Men & Ladies Mon/Fri £7 per day; £5 per round after 3.30pm. Sat & Sun £10 per day; £7 per round after 3.30pm; £25 per week; Juniors under 16 years of age half green fees.
Club Hire:	Not available.
Caddies:	Caddies are not available but the Club does have caddy cars for hire.
Practice Ground:	The Club has a short practice ground.
Catering:	The clubhouse offers full catering facilities by arrangement with the Secretary – Contact Tel. 0542 3226.
Tee Times:	Contact Club Secretary – Tel. 0542 3226.
Handicap:	A handicap certificate is required.
Handicap Limit:	There is no handicap limit.

BURNTISLAND
GOLF HOUSE CLUB
(ESTABLISHED 1895)
Dodhead, Burntisland, KY3 9EY

Featuring spectacular panoramic views across the Firth of Forth towards Edinburgh, the Burntisland course is one of the many fine layouts along the coast of Fife. It is not overbearingly long and there are some fine holes to offer a perfect holiday challenge. Willie Park Jnr laid out the original course which is set in pleasant parkland high above the Firth.

Secretary:	Mr. Ian McLean Tel. 0592 874093
Professional:	Jack Mongomery
	Tel. 0592 873247
Holes:	18
Length:	5908 yards.
	Par: 70 SSS: 69
Visitors:	There are no restrictions on visitors other than at the time of Club competitions.
Ladies & Juniors:	As for Men.
Parties:	Parties are welcome by arrangement with the Secretary – Tel. 0592 874093. Weekend parties must not exceed 24 players.
Green Fees:	Men & Ladies Mon/Fri £11 per round; £16 per day. Weekend £15 per round; £21 per day. Juniors £3 per round.
Club Hire:	Clubs are not available for hire.
Caddies:	There are no caddies available. Caddy cars are available for hire from the Professional's shop.
Practice Ground:	The Club has a short practice ground.
Catering:	The clubhouse offers full catering facilities except on Mondays and Tuesdays.
Tee Times:	Contact the Professional – Tel. 0592 873247.
Handicap:	A handicap certificate is not required.
Handicap Limit:	There is no handicap limit.

CALLANDER GOLF CLUB
(ESTABLISHED 1880)
Aveland Road, Callander, FK17 8EN

Old Tom Morris had a hand in the early design of this pleasant inland course with its fine views and friendly atmosphere. Length is not the challenge here but there are several ditches and water hazards which demand careful shotmaking. Ideal as a relaxing holiday course amid splendid countryside, Callander has much to offer including two open events – the "Lady of the Lake" and the "Jack Scott and Fiery Cross" which attract many visitors in June and July respectively.

Secretary:	Mr. J. McClements Tel. 0877 30866
Professional:	William Kelly
	Tel. 0877 30975
Holes:	18
Length:	5126 yards.
	Par: 66 SSS: 66
Visitors:	Callander Golf Club welcomes visitors without restriction.
Ladies & Juniors:	There are no restrictions on Lady visitors but Juniors must be accompanied by an adult.
Parties:	Parties are welcome by arrangement with the Secretary. Contact – Tel. 0877 30090. Party numbers are limited on Sundays.
Green Fees:	Men & Ladies £10 per round, £14 at weekends; £15 per day, £19 at weekends; £52 per week. Juniors half adult green fee.
Club Hire:	By arrangement with the Professional.
Caddies:	Caddies are not available but caddy cars are available from the Professional's shop.
Practice Ground:	The Club has a short practice ground.
Catering:	The clubhouse offers full catering facilities.
Tee Times:	By arrangement when booking – Contact Tel. 0877 30925.
Handicap:	A handicap certificate is required.
Handicap Limit:	There is no handicap limit.

Callander Golf Club

CARDROSS GOLF CLUB
(ESTABLISHED 1895)
Main Road, Cardross, Dunbartonshire, G72 5LB

Set in rolling parkland the Cardross Golf Club is a fine test of golf at any level. It is not overly long at just over 6400 yards but with soft springy turf there is little run on the fairway for most of the year and the course plays its full length. Willie Fernie from Troon was responsible for the original layout in 1895. There are fine views of the Dunbartonshire countryside to complement the excellent facilities at this old and respected club.

Secretary:	Mr. Robert Evans, C.A. Tel. 0389 841 754
Professional:	Robert Craig
	Tel. 0389 841350
Holes:	18
Length:	6466 yards.
	Par: ?? SSS: 71
Visitors:	Cardross Golf Club welcomes visitors on weekdays only.
Ladies & Juniors:	As for men.
Parties:	Parties are welcome by arrangement with the Secretary – Tel. 0389 841754.
Green Fees:	£13 per round; £20 per day.
Club Hire:	Club hire is not available.
Caddies:	There are no caddies available. Caddy cars are available for hire from the Professional's shop.
Practice Ground:	The Club has a short practice ground.
Catering:	The Clubhouse offers full catering facilities except on Mondays.
Tee Times:	Contact the Professional – Tel. 0389 841350.
Handicap:	A handicap certificate is not required.
Handicap Limit:	There is no handicap limit.

CARNOUSTIE GOLF LINKS
(ESTABLISHED c.1500's)
Links Parade, Carnoustie, DD7 7JE

One of the great championship links of the world Carnoustie has been host to the Open Championship five times and is considered to have one of the toughest finishes in golf. James Braid was responsible for the present layout but some minor alterations have been made in recent years, principally at the 9th and 11th as well as to some bunkering. Carnoustie will host the 1992 Amateur Championship.

Secretary:	Mr. E.J.C. Smith Tel. 0241 53789 Fax. 0241 52720
Professional:	Carnoustie has no attached Professional.
Holes:	18
Length:	6936 yards Par: 72 SSS: 74
Visitors:	Carnoustie welcomes visitors but there are restrictions at weekends and on Monday mornings and at certain other times. Details from the Secretary's Office – Tel. 0241 53789.
Ladies & Juniors:	Restrictions apply as for men.
Parties:	Parties are welcome by arrangement with the Secretary' Office – Contact Tel. 0241 53789.
Green Fees:	Men & Ladies £31 per round. Juniors £15.50 per round.
Club Hire:	By arrangement with local golf shops.
Caddies:	Caddies can be arranged by arrangement with the caddie master. Contact – Tel. 0241 53789.
Practice Ground:	The club has a full length practice ground but not adjacent to the 1st tee.
Catering:	Catering arrangements can be made with one of the local clubs.
Tee Times:	Contact the Secretary's Office – Tel. 0241 53789.
Handicap:	A handicap certificate is required.
Handicap Limit:	Men 20; Ladies 28; Juniors – Boys 20; Girls 28.

Crail Golfing Society's 5th hole

CRAIL GOLFING SOCIETY
(ESTABLISHED 1786)
Balcomie Clubhouse, Crail, Fife, KY10 3XN

One of the oldest golf clubs in the world, Crail also has a reputation of being one of the friendliest. Set on a perfect stretch of links on the Fife coast only a few miles from St Andrews the course is not long but it is tight and interesting and when the wind blows it is as difficult as anyone could wish. Crail is home to the unique Ranken Todd Bowl invitation event in which the winning team must play at least three rounds on the same day.

Secretary:	Mrs. C. W. Penhale Tel. 0333 50686
Professional:	Graeme Lennie
	Tel. 0333 50960
Holes:	18
Length:	5720 yards
	Par: 69 SSS: 68
Visitors:	Crail Golfing Society welcomes visitors without restriction.
Ladies & Juniors:	No restrictions.
Parties:	Parties are welcome by arrangement with the Secretary/Manager – Contact Tel. 0333 50686 except during the last two weeks in July and first two weeks in August.
Green Fees:	Men & Ladies £13.50 per round; £16.50 per day; Weekends £19.50 per round; £24.50 per day; £67.50 per week (5 days); Juniors £7.50 per round; weekends full green fees.
Club Hire:	Clubs are available for hire from the Professional's shop.
Caddies:	Available by prior arrangement. Caddy cars are available for hire.
Practice Ground:	The Club has a full length practice ground.
Catering:	The clubhouse offers full catering facilities.
Tee Times:	Contact the Professional – Tel. 0333 50960.
Handicap:	No handicap certificate required.
Handicap Limit:	None.

CRUDEN BAY GOLF CLUB

(ESTABLISHED 1899)

Cruden Bay, Peterhead, Aberdeenshire, AB42 7NN

This is traditional style links golf at its very best with many blind shots and a delight to play. This is a dramatic course laid out by the renowned golf course architect Tom Simpson, and when the wind blows it is no place for the faint of heart. There is as much challenge here on the Aberdeenshire coast as anyone could wish for. The club was the base for many years of the flamboyant Scottish Ryder Cup Player Eric Brown.

Secretary:	Mr. Ian A. D. McPherson Tel. 0779 812285
Professional:	David Symington Tel. 0779 812414
Holes:	27
Length:	18–6370 yards 9–4710 yards
	Par: 70 SSS: 71 Par: 64 SSS: 62
Visitors:	Cruden Bay Golf Club welcomes visitors except between 4.30pm & 6.30pm on Wednesdays or on competition days and before 3.30pm at weekends.
Ladies & Juniors:	Restrictions as for men.
Parties:	Parties are welcome except at weekends by arrangement with the Secretary – Tel. 0779 812285.
Green Fees:	Men & Ladies £16.50 per day; Weekends £22.50 per day; £67 per week. Juniors £6.50 per day; weekends £8.50; £31 per week.
Club Hire:	Clubs are available for hire from the Professional's shop.
Caddies:	Caddies are available by prior arrangement. Caddy cars are available for hire.
Practice Ground:	The club has both a full length and a short practice ground.
Catering:	The clubhouse offers full catering facilities.
Tee Times:	Contact Club Secretary Tel. 0779 812285.
Handicap:	No handicap certificate is required midweek but a certificate is required at weekends.
Handicap Limit:	Men 28; Ladies 36; Juniors 28.

Cruden Bay course, 7th, 8th and 16th holes

DUNBAR GOLF CLUB
(ESTABLISHED 1794)
East Links, Dunbar, East Lothian, EH42 1LP

This is another of Scotland's ancient links. It is a classic out-and-back arrangement with a loop around the turn in much the same fashion as the Old Course at St Andrews. When the wind blows the problem of keeping the ball in play with out-of-bounds threatening on many of the holes is manifest. But it is thrilling and historic golf alongside the majesty of the Firth of Forth.

Secretary:	Mr. A. Poole Tel. 0368 62317
Professional:	Derek Small
	Tel. 0368 62086
Holes:	18
Length:	6426 yards
	Par: 71 SSS: 71
Visitors:	Dunbar Golf Club welcomes visitors without restriction.
Ladies & Juniors:	No restrictions.
Parties:	Parties are welcome except on Thursdays by arrangement with the Secretary – Contact Tel. 0368 62317.
Green Fees:	Men & Ladies and Juniors £18 per day; Weekends £30 per day.
Club Hire:	Clubs are available for hire from the Professional's shop.
Caddies:	Caddies are available by prior arrangement and caddy cars available for hire. Contact – Tel. 0368 62086.
Practice Ground:	The club has a short practice ground.
Catering:	The clubhouse offers full catering facilities.
Tee Times:	Contact the Professional – Tel. 0368 62086.
Handicap:	No handicap certificate is required.
Handicap Limit:	None.

DUNFERMLINE GOLF CLUB
(ESTABLISHED 1887)
Pitfirrane, Crossford, Dunfermline

The kingdom of Fife is rightly famous for its seaside links courses where golf was nurtured over the centuries. But the county has many fine inland courses, among them the picturesque parkland layout of the Dunfermline Golf Club at Pitfirrane. It is a club with a long tradition dating back to 1887 and is set in rolling woodland on the outskirts of the historic town of Dunfermline. It is not long but always a joy to play.

Secretary:	Mr. Hamish Matheson Tel. 0383 723534
Professional:	Steve Craig
	Tel. 0383 723534
Holes:	18
Length:	6217 yards.
	Par: 71 SSS: 70
Visitors:	Dunfermline Golf Club welcomes visitors Mondays to Fridays between 10am and 12 noon and 2pm and 4pm.
Ladies & Juniors:	Ladies as for men. There is not normally any provision for Junior visitors.
Parties:	Parties to a maximum of 36 are welcome Mondays to Fridays by arrangement with the Secretary – Tel. 0383 723534.
Green Fees:	Men & Ladies £15 per round, £25 per day.
Club Hire:	Club hire is not available.
Caddies:	There are no caddies available. Caddy cars and electronic trolleys are available for hire.
Practice Ground:	The club has a full length practice ground.
Catering:	The Clubhouse offers full catering facilities except on Mondays when bar catering only is available.
Tee Times:	Contact the Professional – Tel. 0383 723534.
Handicap:	An official handicap certificate is required.
Handicap Limit:	Men 28; Ladies 36.

FORFAR GOLF CLUB
(ESTABLISHED 1871)
Cunninghill, Arbroath Road, Forfar DD8 2RI

Old Tom Morris from St Andrews had much to do with the original layout of this fine heathland course. Today it has great stands of pine trees but still retains the springy turf which Old Tom liked so much on his many visits to the Angus course. Relatively modest of length Forfar nonetheless presents a formidable challenge with a couple of outstanding short holes and one or two blind shots thrown in for good measure.

Secretary:	Mr. P. H. Wallace Tel 0307 63773.
Professional:	Peter McNiven Tel. 0307 65638
Holes:	18
Length:	5497 metres
	Par: 69 SSS: 69
Visitors:	Forfar welcomes visitors without restriction.
Ladies & Juniors:	No restrictions.
Parties:	Parties with a maximum number of 30 are welcome except on Saturdays by arrangement with the Secretary Tel. 0307 63773.
Green Fees:	Men & Ladies, Weekdays £12 per round, £18 per day. Sunday £20 per day. Juniors £3 per round, £5 per day.
Club Hire:	Clubs are not available for hire.
Caddies:	There are no caddies available. Caddie cars are available for hire from the professional's shop.
Practice Ground:	The club has practice facilities.
Catering:	The clubhouse offers full catering facilities. Contact the Steward Tel 0307 62120.
Tee Times:	Contact the Starter Tel. 0307 65683.
Handicap:	A handicap certificate is required.
Handicap Limit:	There is no handicap limit.

FORTROSE & ROSEMARKIE GOLF CLUB
(ESTABLISHED 1888)
Ness Road East, Fortrose, Black Isle, Ross-shire

This delightful course is set on a promontory on the Black Isle and has wonderful views over the Cromarty Firth. The course places more emphasis on accuracy than length but like all Scottish links courses can be very difficult when the wind blows. It is a welcoming club with a course perfect as a slight relief from the great challenging courses like Royal Dornoch and Nairn which are within easy reach.

Secretary:	Mrs. M. Collier Tel. 0381 20529
Professional:	Temporarily without a Professional.
Holes:	18
Length:	5973 yards. Par: 71 SSS: 69
Visitors:	Visitors are welcome by arrangement and subject to members needs.
Ladies & Juniors:	As for men.
Parties:	Parties are welcome by arrangement and subject to competitions.
Green Fees:	Adults – £9 per round; £12.50 per day; £33 for 5 days – £44 for 10 days excluding weekends & Public Holidays. Juniors – £5 per round; £7.50 per day; £16.50 for 5 days; £22 for 10 days (excluding Weekends & Public Holidays). Weekends – all classes £12 per round. November to March – Weekdays – Adults £6; Juniors £3; Weekends – Adults £8; Juniors £5.
Club Hire:	Clubs are not available for hire.
Caddies:	Caddies are not available. Caddy cars are available for hire.
Practice Ground:	The club has a full length practice ground.
Catering:	The clubhouse offers full catering facilities by arrangement with the Steward – Tel. 0381 20529.
Tee Times:	Contact the Professional's shop – Tel. 0381 20733.
Handicap:	A handicap certificate is required.
Handicap Limit:	There is no handicap limit.

THE GOLF HOUSE CLUB, ELIE
(ESTABLISHED 1875)
Elie, Fife, KY9 1AS

This delightful course in the picturesque East Neuk of Fife is classic links with wonderful turf and plenty of challenge. It was where the legendary James Braid learned to play his golf and the course remains much as it did in his day. A submarine periscope uniquely monitors play over the hill for the blind opening drive at the start of a memorable golfing journey. The Elie Open Links Championship is traditionally played in August.

Secretary:	Mr. Alexander Sneddon Tel. 0333 330336
Professional:	Robin Wilson Tel. 0333 330301
Holes:	18
Length:	6241 yards.
	Par: 70 SSS: 70
Visitors:	Visitors are welcome from May to September between 10.45 and noon and after 3pm.
Ladies & Juniors:	As above but not allowed in the smoke room.
Parties:	Parties are welcome by prior arrangement with the Secretary – Tel. 0333 330301. Maximum 24 players.
Green Fees:	Mens & Ladies – Weekdays £16 per round, £24 per day; Weekends £22 per round, £32 per day; Week £80. Juniors as men on daily basis, £40 per week.
Club Hire:	Clubs are not available for hire.
Caddies:	Caddies are available by prior arrangement. Caddy cars and electric trollies are available for hire.
Practice Ground:	The club has an excellent full length practice ground.
Catering:	The Clubhouse offers full catering facilities Contact – Tel. 0333 330301.
Tee Times:	Contact the Secretary – Tel. 0333 330301.
Handicap:	No handicap certificate required.
Handicap Limit:	None.

Elie's 4th tee

GRANTOWN ON SPEY
(ESTABLISHED 1890)
Golf Course Road, Grantown on Spey, Morayshire, PH26 3HY

The present layout of the charming course at Grantown on Spey was largely the work of Willie Park in 1910 although just over a decade later James Braid made some improvements. The original nine hole course dates back much earlier. Bobby Cruikshank, who once tied the U.S. Open with Bobby Jones only to lose in the play-off, was a native of Grantown and a famous member of the club, as is the legendary Arnold Palmer who accepted Honorary Membership in 1989. There are marvellous views from many parts of the course.

Secretary:	Mr. Dennis W. Elms Tel. 0479 2715
Professional:	William Mitchell Tel. 0479 2079
Holes:	18
Length:	5745 yards.
	Par: 70 SSS: 67
Visitors:	Grantown on Spey Golf Club welcomes visitors but not before 10am at weekends.
Ladies & Juniors:	As for men.
Parties:	Parties are welcome by arrangement with the Club Secretary – Contact Tel. 0479 2715.
Green Fees:	Men and Ladies – £9 per day midweek; £11 per day weekend; £45 per week; £70 per fortnight. Juniors under 16 – ½ adult green fee.
Club Hire:	Clubs are available for hire by arrangement with the Professional.
Caddies:	There are no caddies available. Caddy cars and electric trollies are available for hire.
Practice Ground:	The Club has a full length practice ground.
Catering:	The Clubhouse offers full catering facilities.
Tee Times:	By arrangement with Mrs McIntosh – Tel. 0479 2235.
Handicap:	A handicap certificate is not required.
Handicap Limit:	There is no handicap limit.

GULLANE GOLF CLUB
(ESTABLISHED 1882)
West Links Road, Gullane, East Lothian, EH31 2BB

There are three courses on this magnificent stretch of Scottish east coast links with the No 1 course the most famous. The climb up the Gullane Hill is well worth the effort for the views across the Firth of Forth and over the mighty Open Championship links of Muirfield are spectacular. The hill makes Gullane unusual for a links course with one or two climbs but they are far from daunting and the pleasure of playing back down is more than adequate recompense. The No 2 and No 3 courses also provide excellent holiday golf.

Secretary:	Mr. A. J. B Taylor Tel. 0620 842255
Professional:	James Hume Tel. 0620 843111
Holes:	18
Length:	No 1 6466 yards. Par: 71 SSS: 71
Visitors:	Visitors are welcome but times are limited especially at weekends.
Ladies & Juniors:	There are no restrictions on Ladies but Juniors must play with an adult.
Parties:	Parties are welcome by arrangement with Bookings Officer – Tel. 0620 8422554 but fourballs are not permitted.
Green Fees:	Men & Ladies £29.60 per round; £44.00 per day; £101.00 per week (5 days on any of the three courses). Juniors half adult green fee.
Club Hire:	Club hire is available.
Caddies:	Caddies are available. Caddy cars and buggies are also available for hire.
Practice Ground:	The club has a full length practice ground.
Catering:	The Clubhouse offers full catering facilities except on Mondays.
Tee Times:	By arrangement with the Bookings Officer on – Tel. 0620 842255.
Handicap:	A handicap certificate is required except for Juniors.
Handicap Limit:	Men 24; Ladies 30.

KILMARNOCK (BARASSIE) GOLF CLUB
(ESTABLISHED 1887)
29 Hillhouse Road, Barassie, Ayrshire

FOUNDED 1887

Kilmarnock Barassie is a qualifying course for the Open Championship when it is held at nearby Royal Troon and has also been the venue for the Scottish Amateur Championship among many other events. It has more of an inland feel about it than pure links despite the fact that it is close to the sea. The name can be slightly confusing since the course lies on the outskirts of Troon and some eight miles or so from Kilmarnock.

Secretary:	Robert L. Bryde Tel. 0292 313920
Professional:	Billy Lockie
	Tel. 0292 311322
Holes:	18
Length:	6473 yards.
	Par: 72 SSS: 71
Visitors:	Visitors are welcome except on Wednesdays, Saturdays and Sundays.
Ladies & Juniors:	As for men.
Parties:	Parties are welcome by arrangement with the Secretary – Tel. 0292 313920 (maximum 60).
Green Fees:	Men £27.00 per round; Ladies £21.00 per round; Juniors £14.00 per round.
Club Hire:	Clubs are available for hire by arrangement with the Professional's shop.
Caddies:	Caddies are not available. Caddy cars are available for hire.
Practice Ground:	The Club has a full length practice ground.
Catering:	The Clubhouse offers full catering facilities.
Tee Times:	Contact Mr David Strawhorn – Tel. 0292 311684.
Handicap:	A handicap certificate is not required.
Handicap Limit:	Men 28; Ladies 36; Juniors 28.

LADYBANK GOLF CLUB
(ESTABLISHED 1879)
Annsmuir, Ladybank, Fife, KY7 7RA

Ladybank is one of Scotland's finest inland courses. Set among glorious stands of pine, heather and gorse it presents a marvellous challenge. There is a premium on accuracy, for to stray from the fairway into the tough Ladybank rough is a situation definitely not to be recommended. It is said that golf clubs let alone balls have been lost in there. Ladybank is an Open Championship qualifying course.

Secretary:	A. M. Dick Tel. 0337 30814
Professional:	Martin J. Gray Tel. 0337 30725
Holes:	18
Length:	6641 yards. Par: 72 SSS: 72
Visitors:	The Club welcomes visitors without restriction.
Ladies & Juniors:	As for men.
Parties:	Parties are welcome on weekdays only by arrangement with the Secretary – Tel. 0337 30814.
Green Fees:	Men & Ladies £20.00 per round; £27.00 per day; £80.00 per week. Juniors £8.00 per day.
Club Hire:	Club are available for hire from the Professional's shop.
Caddies:	Caddies are available during school holiday periods by arrangement. Caddy cars and buggies are available for hire.
Practice Ground:	The Club has a full length practice ground.
Catering:	The Clubhouse offers full catering facilities.
Tee Times:	By arrangement with the Professional – Tel. 0337 30725.
Handicap:	A handicap certificate is preferred.
Handicap Limit:	There is no handicap limit.

Ladybank's 16th hole

LANARK GOLF CLUB
(ESTABLISHED 1851)
The Moor, Whitelees Road, Lanarke, ML11 7RX

One of the world's oldest clubs Lanark is steeped in history yet remains sensitive to the needs of the modern game without detriment to its great traditions. It is a fine heathland course with excellent turf and has been used as an Open Championship qualifying course on many occasions. The present layout in which James Braid had a major influence has remained virtually unchanged since the late 1920's.

Secretary:	Mr. George H. Cuthill Tel. 0555 3219
Professional:	Ron Wallace
	Tel. 0555 61456
Holes:	18
Length:	6423 yards.
	Par: 70 SSS: 71
Visitors:	The Club welcomes visitors on weekdays only and as members guests only at weekends.
Ladies & Juniors:	As for men.
Parties:	Parties are welcome on weekdays only but not on public holidays by arrangement with the Secretary – Tel. 0555 3219.
Green Fees:	£16 per round; £24 per day all categories.
Club Hire:	Club are not available for hire.
Caddies:	Caddies are available by arrangement. Caddy cars and one buggie are available for hire.
Practice Ground:	The Club has practice facilities.
Catering:	The Clubhouse offers full catering facilities during the summer months and from Thursdays to Sundays inclusive during winter months. Contact 0555 65261.
Tee Times:	Contact – Tel. 0555 2349.
Handicap:	A handicap certificate is required.
Handicap Limit:	There is no handicap limit.

LEVEN GOLFING SOCIETY
(ESTABLISHED 1958)
Links Road, Leven, Fife, KY8 4HS

Leven Golfing Society was born out of the historic Innerleven Club which dates back to 1820 and was one of the very earliest golf clubs. The Club plays over a classic links course with pure, traditional turf offering as stiff a challenge as anyone could wish for. It has been a regular qualifying course for the Open Championship when held at St Andrews in recent times and it is the home of the Standard Life Amateur Champion Medal which lays claim to being the oldest open amateur strokeplay championship in the world.

Secretary:	Mr. John W. Bennett Tel. 0333 26096
Professional:	George Finlayson Tel. 0333 26381
Holes:	18
Length:	6435 yards. Par: 71 SSS: 71
Visitors:	The Club welcomes visitors on arrangement with the Secretary – Tel. 0333 26096. There are no course restrictions for men.
Ladies & Juniors:	There are various course restrictions on Ladies and Juniors details of which are available from the Starter – Tel. 0333 21390.
Parties:	Parties are welcome except on Saturdays. Arrangement must be made with the Links Secretary Mr Brian Jackson – Tel. 0333 28859.
Green Fees:	Men & Ladies £13 per round; £18 per day. Weekends £18 per round; £25 per day. Juniors £3 per round.
Club Hire:	Clubs are available for hire.
Caddies:	Caddies can be arranged. Caddy cars are availabe for hire.
Practice Ground:	The Links has a short practice ground.
Catering:	The Clubhouse offers full catering facilities.
Tee Times:	By arrangement with the Starter – Tel. 0333 21390.
Handicap:	A handicap certificate is not required.
Handicap Limit:	There is no handicap limit.

The links at Leven Golfing Society

LONGNIDDRY GOLF CLUB
(ESTABLISHED 1921)
Links Road, Longniddry, East Lothian, EH32 0NL

Although it has fine views of the Firth of Forth Longniddry makes little pretence to being a links course. Lush fairways give it more the feel of a parkland layout and it is not too testing in terms of length. Weekday visitors receive a warm welcome in the friendly Longniddry clubhouse. The course was used as a final qualifying course for the 1987 Open Championship and has hosted the PGA Seniors Championship.

Secretary:	G. C. Dempster Tel. 0875 52141
Professional:	John Gray Tel. 08755 52228
Holes:	18
Length:	6219 yards.
	Par: 68 SSS: 70
Visitors:	Visitors are welcome on weekdays only and at weekends by introduction by a member.
Ladies & Juniors:	Restrictions for Lady visitors are the same as for Men but Juniors may play only on introduction by a member and Mondays to Thursdays only.
Parties:	Parties are welcome by arrangement with the Secretary – Tel. 0875 52141.
Green Fees:	Men & Ladies £18 per round; £27 per day; Juniors £2 per day.
Club Hire:	Clubs are available for hire from the Professional's shop.
Caddies:	Caddies are not available. Caddie cars are available for hire.
Practice Ground:	The Club has a short practice ground.
Catering:	The Clubhouse offers full catering facilities except on Fridays when Bar Service only is available.
Tee Times:	Contact the Starter – Tel. 0875 52228.
Handicap:	A handicap certificate is required.
Handicap Limit:	Men 28; Ladies 36; Juniors – Boys 28; Girls 36.

LUNDIN GOLF CLUB
(ESTABLISHED 1869)
9 Golf Road, Lundin Links, Fife, FK8 6BA

The Lundin Golf Club was founded in 1869 and plays over a fine seaside links course on the shores of the Firth of Forth. Designed by James Braid, it has been used as an Open Championship qualifying course on several occasions, was the venue for the World Senior Professional Championship won by Roberto de Vicenzo in 1974 and is the host club for the East of Scotland Stroke Play Championships.

Secretary:	Mr. A.C. McBride Tel. 0333 320202
Professional:	David Webster Tel. 0333 320051
Holes:	18
Length:	6377 yards. Par: 71 SSS: 71
Visitors:	Lundin G.C. welcomes visitors without restriction.
Ladies & Juniors:	As for Men.
Parties:	Parties are welcome by arrangement with the Secretary but restricted to 32 in number.
Green Fees:	Men and Ladies: £16.50 per round; £24 per day; £70 per week. Juniors: £6 per round; £8 per day; £35 per week.
Club Hire:	Clubs are available for hire from the Professional's shop.
Caddies:	Caddies are available by prior arrangement through the professional. Trolleys and electric caddy cars are available for hire.
Practice Ground:	The Club has a full length practice ground.
Catering:	The Clubhouse offers full catering facilities. Contact – Tel. 0333 320202.
Tee Times:	Contact the Secretary– Tel. 0333 320202 or Professional – Tel. 0333 320051.
Handicap:	A national handicap certificate is required.
Handicap Limit:	There is no handicap limit.

The links at the Lundin Golf Club

MACHRIHANISH GOLF CLUB
(ESTABLISHED 1876)
Machrihanish, Cambeltown, Argyll, PA28 6PT

Old Tom Morris believed that Machrihanish was ''designed by the Almighty for playing golf.'' If it was then Old Tom was able to add to the divine inspiration for he was very much involved in the layout of this classic links on the tip of the Mull of Kintyre. It is one of the remotest courses in the whole of Scotland and one of the best.

Secretary:	Mrs. A. Anderson Tel. 0586 81 213
Professional:	Kevin Campbell Tel. 0586 81 277
Holes:	18 (The Club also has a 9-hole course).
Length:	6228 yards. Par: 70 SSS: 70
Visitors:	Visitors are welcome outwith times reserved for members.
Ladies & Juniors:	Ladies as for Men. Juniors must be accompanied by an adult and have maximum handicap of 18.
Parties:	Parties are welcome outwith times reserved for members by arrangement with the Professional – Tel. 0586 81 277.
Green Fees:	Men and Ladies: £12 per round; £15 per day; £16 per day Weekends. £60 per week; £100 per fortnight. 9-Hole Course: £3 per round; £5 per day; £15 per week. Children under 14 half green fee on 9-Hole Course.
Club Hire:	Clubs are available for hire by arrangement.
Caddies:	There are no caddies available. Caddy cars are available for hire.
Practice Ground:	The Club has a full length practice ground.
Catering:	The Club has full catering facilities except on Mondays but arrangements must be made in advance. Contact A. McNee– Tel. 0586 81 213.
Tee Times:	Contact the Professional – Tel. 0586 81 277.
Handicap:	A handicap certificate is required.
Handicap Limit:	Men: 18; Ladies: 36; Juniors: 18. No limit on 9-Hole Course.

Machrihanish Golf Club

MONIFIETH GOLF CLUB

The Links, Monifieth, Dundee

Golf is known to have been played in Monifieth since 1639 and probably before then. Today the links is shared by five local clubs who enjoy classic links golf over two courses. The Medal course has hosted many important championships and is an excellent test of golf. The shorter Ashludie course is an interesting layout and a more relaxing alternative to the challenge of its more famous companion.

Secretary:	Mr. J. A. R. Fraser Tel. 0382 78117
Professional:	Ron McLeod Tel. 0382 532945
Holes:	36
Length:	Medal 6651 yards. Par: 71 SSS: 72 Ashludie 5123 yards.
Visitors:	Visitors are welcome without restriction, Mon to Fri and after 2pm on Sat and 10am on Sun.
Ladies & Juniors:	Ladies as for Men. Juniors must be accompanied by an adult.
Parties:	Parties are welcome by arrangement with the Secretary – Tel. 0382 78117. Parties are limited to 24 players on Sundays.
Green Fees:	Men and Ladies £15 per round; £22.50 per day; Sundays £17 per round; £25.50 per day. £45 per week. Juniors £3.50 per round.
Club Hire:	Clubs are available for hire from the Professional's shop.
Caddies:	Caddies are available but limited. Contact the Professional – Tel. 0382 532945. Caddy cars and a limited number of electric trollies are available for hire.
Practice Ground:	The Links has a short practice ground.
Catering:	Full catering facilities are provided by the Clubs in rotation. Details from the Starter – Tel. 0382 532767.
Tee Times:	Starter – Tel. 0382 532767 or Secretary – Tel. 0382 78117.
Handicap:	Handicap certificates are required for parties of 12 or more.
Handicap Limit:	National limit for all players.

MONTROSE LINKS
(FOUNDED 1562)

Traill Drive, Montrose, Angus

Golf has been played on the links at Montrose for centuries. It is thought the Marquis of Montrose, who was known to be a devotee of the game in the 16th century was responsible for golf developing on the Angus links. Today the town has two courses administered by a Links Trust and used by three member clubs. The medal course is a classic links which has been the host to many important Scottish Championships.

Secretary:	Mrs. Margaret Stewart Tel. 0674 72932
Professional:	Kevin Stables
	Tel. 0674 72634
Holes:	18
Length:	6443 yards.
	Par: 71 SSS: 71
Visitors:	Visitors are welcome at Montrose except on Saturdays and before 10am on Sundays.
Ladies & Juniors:	As for Men.
Parties:	Parties are welcome by arrangement with the Secretary – Tel. 0674 72932.
Green Fees:	Men and Ladies weekdays £10 per round; £16 per day. Weekends £13.50 per round; £21 per day, £40 per week. Juniors £5 per round; £6.50 per day; £20 per week.
Club Hire:	Clubs are available for hire.
Caddies:	Caddies are available by arrangement. Caddy cars are available for hire from the Professional's shop.
Practice Ground:	The Links has a short practice ground.
Catering:	Prior booking for catering is preferred.
Tee Times:	Contact Mrs Margaret Stewart – Tel. 0674 72932.
Handicap:	An official handicap certificate is required.
Handicap Limit:	Men: 24; Ladies: 36; Juniors 28.

The 3rd seen across the 2nd green at Montrose Links

MORAY GOLF CLUB
(FOUNDED 1889)
Stotfield Road, Lossiemouth, Moray, IV31 6QS

Thick gorse lines many of the fairways on this marvellous stretch of historic linksland in Lossiemouth. Old Tom Morris approved the plans for the Old Course in 1889 and the late Sir Henry Cotton designed the New Course which is laid out inside the original course. Like St Andrews the Old Course starts and finishes inside the town itself and the club hosts the Moray Open in the third week in July each year.

Secretary:	Mr. James Hamilton Tel. 0343 812018
Professional:	Alistair Thomson Tel. 0343 813330
Holes:	36
Length:	Old 6643 yards. New 6005 yards.
	Par: 71 SSS: 72 Par: 69 SSS: 69
Visitors:	Visitors are welcome without restriction.
Ladies & Juniors:	No restrictions.
Parties:	Parties are welcome by arrangement with the Secretary – Tel. 0343 812018.
Green Fees:	Old Course: Weekays £18 per day; £12 after 3pm. Weekends £25 per day; £18 after 3pm. £60 per week. New Course: Weekdays £12 per day; £9 after 3pm. Weekends £18 per day; £12 after 3pm. £45 per week.
Club Hire:	Clubs are not available for hire.
Caddies:	There are no caddies available. Caddie cars are available for hire.
Practice Ground:	The Club has a full length practice ground.
Catering:	The Clubhouse provides full catering facilities.
Tee Times:	Visitors can book tee times on the Old Course on Weekdays after 9.30am but not between 1pm and 2pm; Weekends after 10am but not between 1pm and 2pm. A £2 booking fee applies. Contact Mrs D. MacKintosh – Tel. 0343 812018.
Handicap:	A handicap certificate is required.
Handicap Limit:	Men: 24; Ladies: 36; Juniors 36.

MURCAR GOLF CLUB
(FOUNDED 1909)
Bridge of Don, Aberdeen, AB23 8BD

Archie Simpson and James Braid were responsible for the original layout of this fine course with its formidable dunes and occasional blind shots. It lies close to Royal Aberdeen but it displays a different character to its older neighbour. This is golf in a dramatic setting and the strength of its challenge belies its relatively short length particularly when the wind blows as it does so often in this part of the world.

Secretary:	Mr. Robert Matthews Tel. 0224 704354
Professional:	Alan White Tel. 0224 704370
Holes:	18
Length:	6240 yards.
	Par: 71 SSS: 70
Visitors:	Visitors will be advised of restrictions when booking. Contact the Secretary – Tel. 0224 704354.
Ladies & Juniors:	Ladies as for men. Juniors must be accompanied by an adult.
Parties:	Parties are welcome except at weekends. Contact the Secretary – Tel. 0224 704354.
Green Fees:	Men and Ladies £11.50 per round before 11.30am; £18 per day. £20.50 per day at weekends. £44 per week. Juniors £6.50 per round; £12 per day; £24 per week.
Club Hire:	Clubs are not available for hire.
Caddies:	Caddies are not available. Caddie cars are available for hire.
Practice Ground:	The Club has a full length practice ground.
Catering:	The Clubhouse provides full catering facilities except on Tuesdays unless there is a party of 20 ore more.
Tee Times:	Contact the Secretary – Tel. 0224 704354.
Handicap:	There is no current requirement for a handicap certificate but this may change.
Handicap Limit:	There is no handicap limit.

The 18th at Murcar

THE MUSSELBURGH GOLF CLUB

Monktonhall, Musselburgh, EH21 6SA

M.G.C.

Golf has been played at Musselburgh since the days of Mary Queen of Scots and even before. It is historic golfing country but the course which is now the home of the Musselburgh Golf Club at Monktonhall only dates back to 1938. It was designed by James Braid and officially opened in that year by the three times Open Champion, the late Sir Henry Cotton.

Secretary:	Mr. G. McGill Tel. 031 665 2005
Professional:	Tom Stango
	Tel. 031 665 7055
Holes:	18
Length:	6614 yards.
	Par: 71 SSS: 72
Visitors:	Musselburgh Golf Club welcomes visitors without restriction.
Ladies & Juniors:	As for men.
Parties:	Parties are welcome by arrangement with Mr. G. Finlay – Tel. 031 665 2005.
Green Fees:	Mens & Ladies £12 per round; £18 per day. Juniors £3 per round.
Club Hire:	Clubs can be hired by arrangement with the Professional's shop.
Caddies:	Caddies are available by arrangement with the Professional – Tel. 031 665 7055. Caddy cars are available for hire.
Practice Ground:	The Club has a full length practice ground.
Catering:	The Clubhouse offers full catering facilities except on Tuesdays.
Tee Times:	By arrangement with Mr. G. Finlay – Tel. 031 665 2005.
Handicap:	A handicap certificate is required.
Handicap Limit:	There is no handicap limit.

NAIRN GOLF CLUB
(FOUNDED 1887)
Seabank Road, Nairn

This is one of Scotland's great links courses and yet one of its best kept secrets. Set among great stands of whin and heather it provides a magnificent challenge with wonderful putting greens as firm and fast as will be found anywhere. Andrew Simpson laid out the original course in 1887 which was then extended to a plan of Old Tom Morris. The present layout owes most to James Braid who made major improvements and created a course which now hosts many important championships.

Secretary:	Mr. David Patrick Tel. 0667 53208
Professional:	Robin Fyfe
	Tel. 0667 52728
Holes:	18
Length:	6556 yards
	Par: 72 SSS: 71
Visitors:	Nairn Golf Club welcomes visitors without restriction.
Ladies & Juniors:	As for men.
Parties:	Parties are welcome by arrangement with the Secretary – Tel. 0667 53208.
Green Fees:	Men & Ladies £18 per round; £25 per day Monday to Friday; £22 per round; £30 per day weekends. Juniors £9 per day.
Club Hire:	Clubs are available for hire from the Professional's shop.
Caddies:	Caddies are available by arrangement. Caddy cars and electric trollies are available for hire.
Practice Ground:	The Club has a full length practice ground.
Catering:	The Clubhouse offers full catering facilities.
Tee Times:	By arrangement with the Secretary – Tel. 0667 53208.
Handicap:	A handicap certificate is not required.
Handicap Limit:	Men 28; Ladies 36; Juniors: Boys 28; Girls 36.

Nairn Golf Club

NEWTONMORE GOLF CLUB
(FOUNDED 1893)
Golf Course Road, Newtonmore, Highland, PH20 1AT

Newtonmore is renowned as the club with more left-handed players than any other in the world of golf. This comes about through the influence of the Highland team game of shinty at which Newtonmore excels. Many club members can play either right or left handed and because of the influence of the players who stand on the "wrong side" of the ball they invited 1963 Open Champion, Bob Charles, the greatest left-hander in the history of the game, to open the clubhouse extension in 1984.

Secretary:	Mr. Richard J. Cheyne Tel.	05403 592
		05403 878
Professional:	Robert Henderson	Tel. 05403 281
Holes:	18	
Length:	5880 yards.	Par: 70 SSS: 68
Visitors:	Newtonmore Golf Club welcomes visitors without restriction.	
Ladies & Juniors:	As for men.	
Parties:	Parties are welcome by arrangement with the Secretary – Tel. 05403 591/878.	
Green Fees:	Men & Ladies £9 per day Mondays to Fridays; £12 per day weekends; £36 per week. Juniors half adult green fee.	
Club Hire:	Clubs are available for hire from the Professional's shop.	
Caddies:	Caddies are not available. Caddy cars are available for hire.	
Practice Ground:	The Club does not have any practice facilities.	
Catering:	The Clubhouse offers full catering facilities.	
Tee Times:	Contact the Secretary – Tel. 05403 878/328.	
Handicap:	A handicap certificate is not required.	
Handicap Limit:	Men 28; Ladies 36; Juniors: as for adults.	

THE NORTH BERWICK GOLF CLUB
(FOUNDED 1832)
New Club House, Beach Road, North Berwick, East Lothian,
EH39 4BB

This is one of Scotland's most historic clubs which plays over one of the game's most remarkable courses. It is classic and ancient links with blind shots, great ridges across fairways and even a wall to play over. This is golf of the truly traditional kind which demands several encounters to be fully appreciated.

Secretary:	Position vacant Tel. 0620 5040
Professional:	David Huish Tel. 0620 3233
Holes:	18
Length:	6315 yards. Par: 71 SSS: 70
Visitors:	North Berwick welcomes visitors without restriction.
Ladies & Juniors:	As for men.
Parties:	Parties are welcome by arrangement in advance with the Booking Office – Tel. 0620 2135.
Green Fees:	Men & Ladies £15.50 per round; £22.50 per day, Monday to Friday; £22.50 per round; £32.50 per day, weekends and public holidays. Juniors £11.25 per round; £7.75 per day.
Club Hire:	Clubs are available for hire from the Professional's shop.
Caddies:	Caddies are available by arrangement. Caddie cars are available for hire.
Practice Ground:	The club's practice area is not readily accessible to visitors.
Catering:	The Clubhouse offers full catering facilities except on Thursdays when light snacks only are available.
Tee Times:	Contact the Starter only on day of play or day prior to play – Tel. 0620 2666.
Handicap:	A handicap certificate is required.
Handicap Limit:	National handicap limits.

PANMURE GOLF CLUB
(ESTABLISHED 1845)
Burnside Road, Barry, by Carnoustie, Tayside

Golf has been played on the links of Barry and Carnoustie for more than 400 years. Here is to be found the very cradle of the game and the Panmure Club is one of the great defenders of its traditions. The course is a marvellous links set among giant sandhills and is a marvellous examination of shotmaking. Go there and savour the history and the tradition and if the weather is fine it will be an idyllic experience indeed.

Secretary:	Captain J.C. Ray Tel. 0446 53120
Professional:	Tom Shiel
	Tel. 0446 53120
Holes:	18
Length:	6317 yards.
	Par: 70 SSS: 70
Visitors:	Panmure Golf Club welcomes visitors except on Saturdays.
Ladies & Juniors:	Ladies as for men. Juniors accompanied by adult players.
Parties:	Parties are welcome by arrangement with the Secretary – Tel. 0446 53120.
Green Fees:	Men and Ladies £18 per round; £26 per day. Juniors by arrangement.
Club Hire:	Clubs are not available for hire.
Caddies:	Caddies are available by prior arrangement. Caddy cars are available for hire from the professional's shop. Buggies are permitted by prior arrangement.
Practice Ground:	The Club has a short practice ground.
Catering:	The Clubhouse offers full catering facilities except on Mondays when snacks only are available.
Tee Times:	Contact the Secretary – Tel. 0446 53120.
Handicap:	A handicap certificate is not required.
Handicap Limit:	There is no handicap limit.

PITLOCHRY GOLF CLUB
(ESTABLISHED 1909)
Golf Course Road, Pitlochry, Perthshire

In terms of scenery there are few more spectacular courses in the British Isles than the fine inland layout at Pitlochry in the Scottish Highlands. Renowned for its surroundings and for its Highland welcome Pitlochry offers excellent facilities and marvellous catering at modest cost. The views from the course are breathtaking once the first couple of holes have been negotiated. Pitlochry is the home of the Highland Open Amateur Tournaments for Men and Ladies.

Secretary:	Mr. D. C. M. McKenzie Tel. 0796 2114
Professional:	George Hampton Tel. 0796 2792
Holes:	18
Length:	5811 yards. Par: 69 SSS: 68
Visitors:	There are no restrictions on visitors other than at priority times for members. Mon. 4.30pm–5.30pm; Tues. 1.15pm–1.45pm and 4.30pm–6pm; Thurs. 1.15pm–1.45pm and 5pm–6.30pm. Members also have priority before 9.30am at Weekends.
Ladies & Juniors:	As above.
Parties:	Parties are welcome maximum number 60. No play before 9.30am at Weekends. Contact Estate Office – Tel. 0796 2114.
Green Fees:	Men and Ladies: £12 per day; £9 per round at Weekends only. Juniors £5 per day; £9 Sun.
Club Hire:	Clubs are available for hire.
Caddies:	Caddies are available by arrangement. Caddy cars and electric trollies are available for hire.
Practice Ground:	The course has a short practice ground.
Catering:	The clubhouse provides full catering except on Wednesdays.
Tee Times:	Contact the Professional's shop– Tel. 0796 2792.
Handicap:	A handicap certificate is required.
Handicap Limit:	There is no handicap limit.

ROYAL ABERDEEN GOLF CLUB
(FOUNDED 1780)
Balgownie Links, Bridge of Don, Aberdeen, AB 23 8AT

Here, hardly a mile outside of the "granite city", is golfing history indeed. The Royal Aberdeen Club was founded as the Society of Golfers at Aberdeen in 1780 and as such is recognised as the sixth oldest golf club in the world. The Balgownie links as befits this heritage are among the most testing to be found anywhere and there are marvellous views, particularly on the front nine holes.

Secretary:	Mr. G. F. Webster Tel. 0224 702571
Professional:	Ronnie MacAskill
	Tel. 0224 702221
Holes:	18
Length:	6377 yards.
	Par: 70 SSS: 70
Visitors:	The Club welcomes visitors except between 4.30 and 6.30pm weekdays and not before 3pm on Saturdays.
Ladies & Juniors:	As for men.
Parties:	Parties are welcome on weekdays and after 3.30pm only on Saturdays and by arrangement with the Professional – Tel. 0224 702221.
Green Fees:	Mens & Ladies £20 per round; £25 per day; £25 per round weekends. Juniors as for adults.
Club Hire:	Clubs are available for hire from the Professional's shop.
Caddies:	Caddies are not available. Caddy cars and electric trollies are available for hire.
Practice Ground:	The Club has practice facilities.
Catering:	The Clubhouse offers full catering facilities.
Tee Times:	Contact the Professional's Shop – Tel. 0224 702221.
Handicap:	A handicap certificate is required.
Handicap Limit:	Men 24; Ladies 28; Juniors 18.

Royal Aberdeen Golf Club

ROYAL BURGESS GOLFING SOCIETY OF EDINBURGH
(FOUNDED 1735)
181 Whitehouse Road, Edinburgh, EH4 6BY

INSTITUTED 1735

Although the Royal Burgess Club dates back to 1735 its present course dates back to the 1890s. The Club originally played on ground on Bruntsfield Links sharing the ground with two other historic clubs, Royal Musselburgh and the Honourable Company of Edinburgh Golfers. The present layout is a fine parkland course noted for the quality of its greens.

Secretary:	Mr. J. P. Audis Tel. 031 339 2075
Professional:	George Yuille
	Tel. 031 339 6474
Holes:	18
Length:	6494 yards.
	Par: 71 SSS: 71
Visitors:	A limited number of visitors are welcomed by letter of introduction.
Ladies & Juniors:	There are no changing facilities for ladies. Junior visitors are not permitted.
Parties:	Parties are welcome by arrangement with the Secretary – Tel. 031 339 2075. Restrictions will be advised on application.
Green Fees:	Mens and Ladies £23 per round; Men £31 per day.
Club Hire:	Clubs are available for hire.
Caddies:	Caddies are available by arrangement. Caddy cars and electric trollies are available for hire.
Practice Ground:	The Club has a short length practice ground.
Catering:	Catering arrangements should be made through the Secretary.
Tee Times:	Contact the Secretary – Tel. 031 339 2075.
Handicap:	A handicap certificate is required.
Handicap Limit:	Men 24; Ladies 24.

ROYAL DORNOCH GOLF CLUB
(FOUNDED 1877)
Golf Road, Dornoch, Sutherland

For wild, natural beauty and formidable challenge the links of Royal Dornoch are unsurpassed anywhere in the world. This is an historic links where records show that golf has been played since at least 1616. Dornoch has a unique atmosphere born out of its remoteness as much as the quality of its layout. Old Tom Morris was involved in the early layout but the man who had most influence on the development of Dornoch was John Sutherland a pioneer of greenkeeping and the Club's secretary for more than fifty years.

Secretary:	Mr. Ian Walker Tel. 0862 810219
Professional:	Willie Skinner
Holes:	18
Length:	6581 yards.
	Par: 70 SSS: 72
Visitors:	The Club welcomes visitors subject to handicap restrictions.
Ladies & Juniors:	Ladies as for Men. Juniors over 16 only.
Parties:	Parties are welcome by arrangement with the Secretary – Tel. 0862 810219.
Green Fees:	On request.
Club Hire:	Clubs are available for hire from the Professional's shop.
Caddies:	Caddies are available by arrangement. Caddy cars and electric trollies are available for hire.
Practice Ground:	The Club has a full length practice ground.
Catering:	The Clubhouse offers full catering facilities except on Mondays.
Tee Times:	By arrangement with the Secretary – Tel. 0862 810219.
Handicap:	A handicap certificate is required.
Handicap Limit:	Men 24; Ladies 35.

Royal Dornoch golf course

ROYAL TROON GOLF CLUB
(FOUNDED 1878)
Troon, Ayrshire, KA10 6EP

Royal Troon is the most notable of the five courses which this lovely Ayrshire town has to offer. The championship course has been the scene of much Open Championship excitement and commands wonderful views across the Firth of Clyde towards the Isle of Arran and the Mull of Kintyre. It is a formidable links and extremely demanding with a back nine the equal of any in golf in terms of ferocity. The Club's other course, the Portland, is slightly less taxing but none the less pleasant for that.

Secretary:	Mr. J. D. Montgomerie Tel. 0292 311555
Professional:	R. Brian Anderson Tel: 0292 313281
Holes:	Old Course 18; Portland Course 18
Length:	Old Course: 6641 yards. Par: 71 SSS: 73 Portland: 6274 yards. Par: 70 SSS: 71
Visitors:	Visitors are welcome with a letter of introduction Mondays to Thursdays only except 9.30am to 11am and 2.30pm to 3.10pm. Other restrictions apply and visitors should contact the Secretary – Tel. 0292 311555.
Ladies & Juniors:	No ladies or juniors allowed to play the Old Course or to enter the clubhouse.
Parties:	Parties are welcome by prior arrangement maximum number 24. Contact the Secretary – Tel. 0292 311555.
Green Fees:	Composite fees. £57 per day – one round each course. Only one round on the Old Course is permitted. £37 per day – Portland Course only.
Club Hire:	Clubs are available for hire.
Caddies:	Caddies are available by arrangement in advance and subject to availability.
Practice Ground:	The Club has practice facilities.

Catering:	The composite green fee includes morning coffee and lunch or high tea. Requirements to be advised one week in advance.
Tee Times:	Contact the Secretary – Tel. 0292 311555.
Handicap:	A handicap certificate is required.
Handicap Limit:	Men 20; Ladies 30 on Portland Course only.

Royal Troon golf course

THE OLD COURSE
(ESTABLISHED c.1400)
St Andrews, Fife

The Old Course at St Andrews is the most famous golf course in the world. It has been the scene of many great championships and is recognised the world over as the home of the game. The St Andrews courses are administered by the Links Joint Management Committee and not as many believe by the Royal and Ancient Golf Club whose clubhouse overlooks the first tee. The Old Course is the classic links course of nine holes out and nine back with shared fairways and large double greens.

Secretary:	Mr. A Beveridge Tel. 0334 77036
Professional:	None.
Holes:	18
Length:	6566 yards.
	Par: 72 SSS: 72
Visitors:	The Old Course welcomes visitors who are members of recognised Golf Club and who hold current handicap certificates.
Ladies & Juniors:	As for men.
Parties:	Parties are welcome by arrangement with the Reservations Office – Tel. 0334 75057.
Green Fees:	Mens, Ladies & Juniors £31 per round.
Club Hire:	Arrangements can be made for club hire.
Caddies:	Caddies are available by arrangement. Caddy cars are available for hire from May to September but are permitted only for afternoon play.
Practice Ground:	St Andrews has practice facilities but not close to the first tee.
Catering:	There are no clubhouse catering facilities.
Tee Times:	By prior arrangement with the reservations office – Tel. 0334 75757. A ballot system operates in the summer.
Handicap:	A current handicap certificate is required.
Handicap Limit:	Men 28; Ladies 36; Juniors 36.

St. Andrew's, the 18th

THE NEW COURSE
(FOUNDED 1896)
St Andrews, Fife

The New Course at St Andrews belies its name for it is not now new at all. It dates back to 1896 and has undergone some changes over the intervening years. There are many who believe it to be even more difficult than its famous sister which is certainly true on some occasions particularly if the Old Course is tackled from forward tees to the more accommodating pin positions normally presented to visitors.

Secretary:	Mr. A. Beveridge Tel. 0334 77036
Professional:	None.
Holes:	18
Length:	6640 yards.
	Par: 71 SSS: 72
Visitors:	There are no restrictions of visitors to the New Course at St Andrews.
Ladies & Juniors:	As for men.
Parties:	Parties are welcome by arrangement with the Reservations Office – Tel. 0334 75057.
Green Fees:	Mens & Ladies £13 per round; £72 per week. Juniors £7 per round; £36 per week.
Club Hire:	Arrangements can be made for club hire.
Caddies:	Caddies are available by arrangement. Caddy cars are available for hire.
Practice Ground:	St Andrews has practice facilities but not close to the first tee.
Catering:	There are no clubhouse catering facilities.
Tee Times:	By arrangement with the reservations Office – Tel. 0334 75757 or by application to the Starter at the course.
Handicap:	A handicap certificate is not required.
Handicap Limit:	There is no handicap limit.

THE JUBILEE COURSE
(FOUNDED 1897)
St Andrews, Fife

Founded the year after the New Course the Jubilee Course was for many years considered the "Ladies" course at St Andrews being somewhat shorter than its bigger sisters. But the course has undergone a massive reconstruction at the hands of the top golf course architect, Donald Steel, and is now a formidable challenge of more than 6800 yards. It remains the St Andrew course closest to the sea.

Secretary:	Mr. A. Beveridge Tel. 0334 77036
Professional:	None.
Holes:	18
Length:	6805 yards.
	Par: 72 SSS: 73
Visitors:	There are no restrictions of visitors to the Jubilee Course at St Andrews.
Ladies & Juniors:	As for men.
Parties:	Parties are welcome by arrangement with the Reservations Office – Tel. 0334 75057.
Green Fees:	Mens & Ladies £13 per round; £72 per week. Juniors £7 per round; £36 per week.
Club Hire:	Arrangements can be made for club hire.
Caddies:	Caddies are available by arrangement. Caddy cars are available for hire.
Practice Ground:	St Andrews has practice facilities but not close to the first tee.
Catering:	There are no clubhouse catering facilities.
Tee Times:	By arrangement with the reservations Office – Tel. 0334 75757 or by application to the Starter at the course.
Handicap:	A handicap certificate is not required.
Handicap Limit:	There is no handicap limit.

The Jubilee Course

The 7th hole on the Eden Course

The Eden Course, 11th hole

THE EDEN COURSE
(FOUNDED 1914)
St Andrews, Fife

The Eden Course at St Andrews built in 1914 on the west side of the railway line which at one time served the old university town was always one of the favourite St Andrews courses. It has always had a charm and character different from its sister courses although it is a good enough test in its own right. Like the Jubilee Course it had been undergoing extensive reconstruction work by Donald Steel as part of new St Andrews links development.

Secretary:	Mr. A. Beveridge Tel. 0334 77036
Professional:	None
Holes:	18
Length:	6315 yards.
	Par: 70 SSS: 70
Visitors:	There are no restrictions of visitors to the Eden Course at St Andrews.
Ladies & Juniors:	As for men.
Parties:	Parties are welcome by arrangement with the Reservations Office – Tel. 0334 75057.
Green Fees:	Mens & Ladies £11 per round; £72 per week. Juniors £36 per week.
Club Hire:	Arrangements can be made for club hire.
Caddies:	Caddies are available by arrangement. Caddy cars are available for hire.
Practice Ground:	St Andrews has practice facilities.
Catering:	There are no clubhouse catering facilities.
Tee Times:	By arrangement with the reservations Office – Tel. 0334 75757 or by application to the Starter at the course.
Handicap:	A handicap certificate is not required.
Handicap Limit:	There is no handicap limit.

SOUTHERNESS GOLF CLUB
(ESTABLISHED 1947)
Southerness, Kirkbean, Dumfries, DG2 8AZ

Despite its relative isolation there are many beating a path to the clubhouse door at Southerness and with justification for this Mackenzie Ross course, built in 1947, is one of the finest in the land. Here there is challenging, natural golf amid heather and bracken exposed to the fickle winds of the Solway Firth. The views from the clubhouse over the hills of Galloway and the Firth are memorable and visitors enjoy a warm Borders welcome.

Secretary:	Major D. D. J. Palmer Tel. 0387 88677
Professional:	None.
Holes:	18
Length:	6554 yards.
	Par: 69 SSS: 72
Visitors:	Visitors are welcome on Weekdays except Tuesdays between 10.00am and 12.00 noon and 2.00pm and 3.00pm. Thursdays between 10.45am and 1.00pm and 2.15pm and 4.30pm. Weekends and Bank Holidays 10.30am and 12.00 noon and 2.30pm and 4.30pm.
Ladies & Juniors:	As for men.
Parties:	Parties are welcome by arrangement with the Secretary – Tel. 0387 88677.
Green Fees:	Weekdays £18 per day; Weekends and Bank Holidays £22 per day.
Club Hire:	Clubs are not available for hire.
Caddies:	There are no caddies available. Caddy cars are available for hire.
Practice Ground:	The Club has a full length practice ground.
Catering:	The Clubhouse offers full catering facilities. Contact Mrs. A. Ring – Tel. 0387 88677.
Tee Times:	Contact the Secretary – Tel. 0387 88677.
Handicap:	An official handicap certificate is required.
Handicap Limit:	There is no handicap limit.

STRATHAVEN GOLF CLUB
(FOUNDED 1908)
Glasgow Road, Strathaven, ML10 6NL

Willie Fernie laid out the original nine holes at Strathaven (pronounced ''Straven'') in 1908. An additional nine were added later by Hamilton Stutt. The course is set in attractive, rolling and wooded countryside just outside the picturesque town of Strathaven south of Glasgow. It is not overly long but a pleasant and stern enough test. The clubhouse has a warm atmosphere and visitors are made very welcome.

Secretary:	Mr. A. W. Wallace Tel. 0357 20421
Professional:	Matthew McCrorie
	Tel. 0357 21812
Holes:	18
Length:	6226 yards.
	Par: 71 SSS: 70
Visitors:	Visitors are welcome at Strathaven weekdays only.
Ladies & Juniors:	Ladies as for men. Juniors must be accompanied by an adult.
Parties:	Parties are welcome on Tuesdays only.
Green Fees:	Mens and Ladies £15 per round; £20 per day. Juniors half the adult green fee.
Club Hire:	Clubs are not available for hire.
Caddies:	There are no caddies available. Caddy cars are available for hire from the Professional's shop.
Practice Ground:	The Club has practice facilities.
Catering:	The Club offers full catering facilities.
Tee Times:	Contact the Secretary – Tel. 0357 20421 or the Professional – Tel. 0357 21812.
Handicap:	An official handicap certificate is required.
Handicap Limit:	Men 28; Ladies 36; Juniors 33.

ENGLAND

Although it is claimed that a golf club was founded at Blackheath in London in 1608 there is no documentary evidence to support it. The earliest date that can be substantiated is 1766. In that year a silver club was donated to the golfers at Blackheath and bears the inscription "August 16, 1766, the gift of Mr Henry Foot to the Honorable Company of Golfers at Blackheath".

Royal Blackheath stands, therefore, as the oldest club in England but there is no doubt the game was played in the south well before then. There is a reference to golf by Catherine of Aragon, the first wife of Henry VIII, in a letter to Cardinal Wolsey in 1513 but it was probably not until the Union of the Crowns in 1603 that the game began to make any impression south of the border.

It was taken there by the Royal Household when the thrones were united under James VI of Scotland as James I of England. There is argument as to whether the king introduced the game to the neighbourhood of Greenwich or to Blackheath but there is no doubt that golf was played later at Westminster and at Molesey Hurst.

The Royal connections are obvious for St James's Palace was close to Westminster and Molesey Hurst was close to Hampton Court.

But while there were pockets of golf in England in the 18th century it would be another hundred years before there was a significant spread. The oldest existing course in England is at Westward Ho! in Devon where the club was formed in 1864. It was here that the great J. H. Taylor learned to play his golf as a boy and where, too, he played the last golf of his very full life.

Westward Ho! is significant as the oldest course in England but the club which is ranked as being the most important in the development of the game in the south is the Royal Liverpool Club at Hoylake.

It was here that the Amateur Championship was born; it was here that the great amateur players like John Ball, Harold Hilton and Charles Hutchings made their impact on the game and it was here that Bobby Jones won the Open Championship in his historic Grand Slam year of 1930.

Today there are well over 1400 courses in England.

ALWOODLEY GOLF CLUB
(ESTABLISHED 1907)
Wigton Lane, Alwoodley, Leeds, LS17 8SAA

Harry S. Colt and Dr Alister Mackenzie, famous for his work with Bobby Jones at Augusta National, were responsible for this layout in fine golfing country. Built on light, sandy soil the course is always firm and dry and the turf crisp. It is a fine test of golf although not normally over-demanding but when the wind blows it is a match for anyone.

Hon. Secretary:	Mr. T. G. Turnbull Tel. 0532 681680
Professional:	J. Green
	Tel. 0532 689603
Holes:	18
Length:	6686 yards.
	Par: 72 SSS: 72
Visitors:	Visitors are welcome by previous arrangement with the Club – Tel. 0532 681680.
Ladies & Juniors:	No restrictions other than as above.
Parties:	Parties are welcome by arrangement with the Club – Tel. 0532 681680.
Green Fees:	£30 per round or day for all players.
Club Hire:	Club are available for hire.
Caddies:	No caddies are available.
Practice Ground:	The Club has practice facilities.
Catering:	Full catering is available by arrangement with the Club – Tel. 0532 681680.
Tee Times:	By arrangement with the Club Secretary – Tel. 0532 681680.
Handicap:	A national handicap is required for all visiting players.
Handicap Limit:	There is no handicap limit.

BARNHAM BROOM HOTEL
GOLF & COUNTRY CLUB

Norwich, Norfolk, NR9 4DD

The Barnham Broom Golf and Country Club offers two challenging eighteen holes courses in a beautiful Norfolk setting. The club has a conference and leisure centre and is a noted venue for golf instruction being base for the widely-acclaimed Peter Ballingall Golf Schools. This very hospitable club with many additional sports facilities has hosted PGA European Satellite Tour events since 1987.

Managing Director:	Mr. A. Long, Tel. 060 545 393, Fax. 060 545 8224
Director of Golf:	Peter Ballingall, Tel. 060 545 393 (Ext. 132)
Club Professional:	S. Beckham
Holes:	36
Length:	Valley: 6470 yards. Par: 72 SSS: 71
	Hill: 6628 yards. Par: 72 SSS: 72
Visitors:	Barnham Broom Golf & Country Club welcomes visitors without restriction.
Ladies & Juniors:	There are no restrictions on Ladies or Juniors.
Parties:	Parties are welcome without restriction by arrangement with the Director of Golf. Contact – Tel. 060 545 393 (Ext. 132).
Green Fees:	Men & Ladies £22.50 per round; £27.50 per day. Juniors £12 per round; £15 per day. Weekly rates are available on application to the Director of Golf.
Club Hire:	By arrangement with the Club Professional.
Caddies:	Caddies are not available.
Practice Ground:	A full length practice ground is available.
Catering:	The club is part of a hotel complex and has full catering facilities.
Tee Times:	Contact the Golf Shop – Tel. 060 545 393.
Handicap:	Handicap certificate not required.
Handicap Limit:	None.

THE BELFRY
(ESTABLISHED 1977)
Lichfield Road, Wishaw, North Warwickshire, B78 9PR

The Belfry

The Belfry won a unique place in European golf history by virtue of the dramatic Ryder Cup matches played there in 1985 and 1989. The Brabazon Course over which the matches were played is a stern test indeed from the back tees but much more manageable when tackled from further forward. The shorter Derby Course is a worthy counterfoil. The Belfry has been selected to host the 1993 Ryder Cup Matches.

Secretary:	Mr. Chris Hart, Tel. 0675 470301, Fax. 0675 470256
Professional:	Peter McGovern, Tel. 0675 470301
Holes:	36
Length:	Brabazon: 6975 yards. Par: 73 SSS: 72 Derby: 6127 yards. Par: 70 SSS: 70
Visitors:	Visitors are welcome without restriction.
Ladies & Juniors:	No restrictions.
Parties:	Parties are welcome by arrangement with the Golf Office – Contact Tel. 0675 470301.
Green Fees:	The Derby Course – Mon/Fri – £20.00 per round; Sat/Sun/Bank Hol. £25.00 per round. Two rounds £30.00. Sat/Sun/Bank Hol. £40.00. The Brabazon Course – Mon/Fri – £45.00 per round. Sat/Sun/Bank Hol. £50.00 per round. Other package arrangements available on request.
Club Hire:	Club hire is available from the Professional's shop.
Caddies:	Caddies are available by arrangement.
Practice Ground:	A full length practice ground is available.
Catering:	There are full catering facilities.
Tee Times:	Contact the Golf Office – Tel. 0675 470301.
Handicap:	A handicap certificate is required.
Handicap Limit:	Men 24; Ladies 32; Juniors 24.

The Belfry

BERKHAMSTED GOLF CLUB
(ESTABLISHED 1890)
The Common, Berkhamsted, Herts HB4 2QB

Set in open heath in the Chiltern Hills Berkhamsted is one of England's most natural golf courses. Visitors will find no bunkers to test their prowess with the sand iron but they will find gorse and heather aplenty. On seven holes they will also find Grim's Dyke presenting itself as a formidable hazard. This ancient earthwork has a heather bank as high as a man with a 4 ft deep grassy ditch. The Club hosts the Berkhamsted Trophy traditionally the opening amateur event of the year.

Secretary:	Mr. I. D. Wheater Tel. 0442 865832
Professional:	Basil Proudfoot Tel. 0442 865851
Holes:	18
Length:	6605 yards.
	Par: 71 SSS: 72
Visitors:	Berkhamsted welcomes visitors subject to there being room on the course.
Ladies & Juniors:	No restrictions.
Parties:	Parties, maximum number 45, are welcome by arrangement with the Secretary Tel. 0442 865832
Green Fees:	Men & Ladies £22.50 per round, £32.50 per day, weekends £49. Juniors £3.75 per round.
Club Hire:	Clubs are not available for hire.
Caddies:	There are no caddies available. Caddie cars and electric trollies are subject to winter ban.
Practice Ground:	The Club has full length and short length practice grounds.
Catering:	The clubhouse offers full catering facilities except on Mondays and Tuesdays.
Tee Times:	Contact the Secretary – Tel. 0442 865832.
Handicap:	An official handicap certificate is required.
Handicap Limit:	There is no handicap limit.

THE BERKSHIRE GOLF CLUB
(ESTABLISHED 1928)
Swinley Road, Ascot, Berkshire, SL5 8AY

Golf at The Berkshire is among the very best to be found inland anywhere in the British Isles. It is classic heathland golf with marvellous challenge over the Red and Blue courses. Herbert Fowler built the courses on Crown land in the late 1920's. The club plays host annually to the Berkshire Trophy, one of golf's most prestigious amateur events.

Secretary:	Mr. P. D. Clarke Tel. 0344 21496
Professional:	K. A. MacDonald Tel. 0344 22351
Holes:	36
Length:	Red Course: 6369 yards.
	Par: 72 SSS: 70
	Blue Course: 6260 yards.
	Par: 71 SSS: 70
Visitors:	The Berkshire Gold Club welcomes visitors either by introduction by members or by arrangment with the Secretary – Contact Tel. 0344 21496.
Ladies & Juniors:	Arrangements as for men.
Parties:	Parties are welcome by arrangement with the Secretary – Contact Tel. 0344 21496.
Green Fees:	Men & Ladies £40 per round; £55 per day; Juniors under 17 years of age £12 per day.
Club Hire:	By arrangement with the Professional's Shop.
Caddies:	Caddies are available by prior arrangement. Contact – Tel. 0344 22627. Caddy cars, electric trollies and buggies are available.
Practice Ground:	The Club has a full length practice ground.
Catering:	The clubhouse offers full catering facilities except on Mondays when sandwiches only are available.
Tee Times:	Contact the Secretary – Tel. 0344/21496.
Handicap:	A handicap certificate is required.
Handicap Limit:	Men 28; Ladies 36; Juniors 28/36.

The Berkshire Golf Club

BROADSTONE (DORSET) GOLF COURSE
(ESTABLISHED 1898)
Wentworth Drive, Broadstone, Dorset, BH18 8DR

The original course at Broadstone was laid out by Willie Park but it was later modernised by Harry S. Colt. Set in splendid countryside there are marvellous views of Poole Harbour, the Channel and the Purbeck Hills. Although essentially heathland with masses of heather and gorse the course also has fine stands of pine, oak and chestnut and spectacular rhododendron when in bloom. It is also a very fine challenge despite its shortish length.

Secretary:	Mr. J. M. Cowan Tel. 0202 692595
Professional:	N. Tokely
	Tel. 0202 692835
Holes:	18
Length:	6183 yards.
	Par: 70 SSS: 69
Visitors:	The Club welcomes visitors by prior arrangement with the Secretary – Contact Tel. 0202 692595.
Ladies & Juniors:	No restrictions on Lady players; Juniors must be accompanied by an adult.
Parties:	Parties are welcome by arrangement with the Secretary – Contact Tel. 0202 692595.
Green Fees:	Men & Ladies £21 per round; £25 per day; Juniors £10.50 per round; £12.50 per day.
Club Hire:	By arrangement with the Professional.
Caddies:	Caddies are not available. Electric trollies can be arranged.
Practice Ground:	The Club has a full length practice ground.
Catering:	The clubhouse offers full catering facilities.
Tee Times:	Contact William Hay – Tel. 0202 693363.
Handicap:	A handicap certificate is required.
Handicap Limit:	Men 24; Ladies 36; Juniors 24.

BURNHAM & BERROW GOLF CLUB
(ESTABLISHED 1890)
St Christophers Way, Burnham-on-Sea, Somerset, TA8 2PE

There is fine links golf to be found here in Somerset among the great sandhills near Bridgwater. From the summit of each of the great mountains of sand there are spectacular views, to the one side a range of hills with the Cheddar Gorge in the distance and to the other the Bristol Channel. Many of the blind shots of the original design have passed into history but a few remain to offer a great traditional challenge.

Secretary:	Mrs. E. L. Sloman Tel. 0278 785760
Professional:	Mark Crowther-Smith Tel. 0278 7845454
Holes:	18
Length:	6327 yards. Par: 71 SSS: 72
Visitors:	Burnham & Berrow Golf Club welcomes visitors who are members of recognised golf clubs and hold national handicaps.
Ladies & Juniors:	No restrictions except as above.
Parties:	Parties are welcome by arrangement with the Secretary – Contact Tel. 0278 785760 with the same restrictions as individual visitors.
Green Fees:	Men & Ladies £36 per round; £36 per day; £150 per week. Juniors half adult green fee.
Club Hire:	By arrangement with the Professional's shop.
Caddies:	Available by prior arrangement. Contact – Tel. 0278 784545.
Practice Ground:	The Club has a full length practice ground.
Catering:	The Clubhouse offers full catering facilities but evening meals must be booked in advance.
Tee Times:	Contact Club Secretary – Tel. 0278 785760.
Handicap:	A handicap certificate is required.
Handicap Limit:	Men 22; Ladies 30; Juniors – Boys 22; Girls 30.

Burnham and Berrow Golf Club

CHURCH STRETTON GOLF CLUB
(ESTABLISHED 1898)
Hunters Moon, Trevor Hill, Church Stretton, Shropshire,
SY6 6JH

For lovers of hillside golf there is much to delight in at
Church Stretton perched on the lower slopes of the
Longmynd thirteen miles to the west of Shrewsbury.
Play is very much up hill and down dale giving full
advantage to the marvellous views which abound on this
type of course. James Braid laid out the course just
before the turn of the century.

Secretary:	Mr. D. Broughton Tel. 0694 722633
Professional:	I. Doran (In Season) Tel. 0694 722633
Holes:	18
Length:	5008 yards. Par: 66 SSS: 65
Visitors:	Church Stretton Golf Club welcomes visitors without restriction.
Ladies & Juniors:	No restrictions.
Parties:	Parties are welcome by arrangement with the Hon. Secretary – Contact Tel. 0694 722633.
Green Fees:	Men & Ladies £10 per round; £15 weekends per round. Juniors £5 per round; £7.50 weekends.
Club Hire:	Clubs are not available for hire.
Caddies:	No arrangements can be made for caddies and there are no caddy cars available for hire.
Practice Ground:	The Club has no practice facilities.
Catering:	Catering facilities are available by arrangement with the club steward – April to November only.
Tee Times:	Contact Hon. Secretary – Tel. 0694 722833.
Handicap:	A handicap certificate is required.
Handicap Limit:	None.

FORMBY GOLF CLUB
(ESTABLISHED 1884)
Golf Road, Formby, Liverpool, L37 1LQ

Formby is one of the many fine links courses which run in a line up the Lancashire coast and represent some of the best golf England has to offer. Although there are great sand dunes there are also trees to provide some protection from the sea breezes. Although lady visitors are welcome on the course it should be remembered that the clubhouse itself is very much ''men only''. The ladies have their own clubhouse at Formby.

Secretary:	Mr A. Thirlwell Tel. 07048 72164
Professional:	Clive Harrison
	Tel. 07048 73090
Holes:	18
Length:	6695 yards.
	Par: 72 SSS: 73
Visitors:	Formby Golf Club welcomes visitors except on Wednesday, Saturdays and Sundays.
Ladies & Juniors:	As for men.
Parties:	Parties are welcome by arrangement with the Secretary – Contact Tel. 07048 72164.
Green Fees:	Men & Ladies £36 per day. Juniors to be arranged.
Club Hire:	Clubs are not available for hire.
Caddies:	Caddies are available by prior arrangement. Caddy cars are available for hire.
Practice Ground:	The club has a short practice ground.
Catering:	The clubhouse offers full catering facilities except on Mondays. Gentlemen must wear jacket and tie in the dining room.
Tee Times:	Contact Mrs F. Gates-Smith – Tel. 07048 72164.
Handicap:	A handicap certificate is required.
Handicap Limit:	Men 24; Ladies 30; Juniors 28.

Ferndown Golf Club

FERNDOWN GOLF CLUB
(ESTABLISHED 1912)
119 Golf Links Road, Ferndown, Dorset, BH22 8BU

Laid out amid pines and heather the Old Course at Ferndown has some wonderful views despite its residential setting. It is a course synonymous with the Alliss name and was for some years home to Percy and son Peter now renowned as a golf commentator. This is a pleasant rather than a testing layout, the design of which is credited to the great amateur player Harold Hilton, and is perfect for relaxed holiday golf in fine surroundings.

Secretary:	Mr. G. Robertson, Tel. 0202 874602, Fax. 0202 873926
Professional:	D. Sewell Tel. 0202 873825
Holes:	27
Length:	6442 yards. Par: 71 SSS: 71
Visitors:	Ferndown Golf Club welcomes visitors subject to handicap restrictions.
Ladies & Juniors:	As for men.
Parties:	Parties are welcome on Tuesday's and Friday's only by arrangement with the Secretary/Manager – Contact Tel. 0202 874602.
Green Fees:	Men, Ladies & Juniors £30 per day.
Club Hire:	Clubs and caddy cars are available for hire.
Caddies:	Caddies are not available.
Practice Ground:	The Club has a full length practice ground.
Catering:	The clubhouse offers full catering facilities.
Tee Times:	Contact Secretary/Manager – Tel. 0202 874602.
Handicap:	A handicap certificate is required.
Handicap Limit:	Men 28; Ladies 36; Juniors 28.

GANTON GOLF CLUB
(ESTABLISHED 1891)
Ganton, Nr. Scarborough, North Yorkshire, YO12 4PA

Ganton is one of the few remaining pure heathland courses in the British Isles and one of the great inland courses of the world. Dr. Alister Mackenzie was one of the many eminent architects and players who have left their mark on the course since it came into being in 1891. The legendary Harry Vardon, who also contributed to the development of the course, was the Club's professional for several years. Ganton puts a premium on accuracy rather than length.

Secretary:	Air Vice Marshal R. G. Price C. B. Tel. 0944 70329
Professional:	Garry Brown Tel. 0944 70260
Holes:	18
Length:	6822 yards. Par: 71 SSS: 74
Visitors:	Visitors are welcome after 9.30am and before 2.15pm but must be members of bona fide golf clubs with official handicaps.
Ladies & Juniors:	As for men.
Parties:	Parties are welcome by prior arrangement with the Secretary – Contact Tel. 0944 70329.
Green Fees:	Green fees are available on application only.
Club Hire:	Club hire is available from the Professional's shop.
Caddies:	There are no caddies available. Caddy cars, electric trollies and two buggies are available for hire.
Practice Ground:	The Club has a full length practice ground.
Catering:	The Club offers full catering facilities. However, the dining room closes at 6pm unless prior arrangements are made for a party booking.
Tee Times:	Contact Mrs. J. Hill – Tel. 0944 70329.
Handicap:	A handicap certificate is required.
Handicap Limit:	Men 28; Ladies 36; Juniors by arrangement.

The club house at Ganton

GOG MAGOG GOLF CLUB

Shelford Bottom, Cambridge, CB2 4AB

The famous Gog Magog Club outside Cambridge is set in delightful countryside high on the heath above the university town. Fine turf and a warm welcome await visitors as well as an excellent challenge despite the modest length of the Old course layout. Spectacular views abound from all parts of the course and there is good all-year-round golf here well worth sampling.

Secretary:	Mr. J. E. Ritchie Tel. 0223 247626
Professional:	Ian Bamborough
	Tel. 0223 246058
Holes:	27
Length:	Old: 5532 yards.
	Par: 70 SSS: 70
	New: (9) 5403 yards.
	Par: 68 SSS: 68
Visitors:	Visitors are welcome subject to handicap restrictions.
Ladies & Juniors:	As above.
Parties:	Parties are welcome on Tuesdays and Thursdays by prior arrangement with the Secretary – Tel. 0223 247626.
Green Fees:	Old Course: Men & Ladies £25 per round; £30 per day. New Course: Men & Ladies £15 per day.
Club Hire:	Clubs are not available for hire.
Caddies:	There are no caddies available. Caddy cars and electric trollies are available for hire.
Practice Ground:	The club has a full length practice ground.
Catering:	The clubhouse offers full catering facilities with no restrictions.
Tee Times:	By arrangement with the Professional – Contact Tel. 0223 246058.
Handicap:	A handicap certificate is required.
Handicap Limit:	Old Course – Men 22; Ladies 27; Juniors 18. New Course – Men 28; Ladies 36; Juniors 28.

HUNSTANTON GOLF CLUB
(ESTABLISHED 1891)
Golf Course Road, Old Hunstanton, Norfolk, PE36 6JQ

One of the great challenges on the east coast of England, Hunstanton has undergone many changes since it was founded as a nine-hole course a century ago. It was one of the many courses James Braid was asked to make alterations to after it was extended to 18 holes. James Sherlock, a famous professional at the club for many years, brought some new ideas to the course in the mid 1920's and there have been additional improvements since. It remains a course of great quality and a joy to play.

Secretary:	Mr. R. H. Cotton Tel. 0485 532811
Professional:	John Carter Tel. 0485 532751
Holes:	18
Length:	6670 yards. Par: 72 SSS: 72
Visitors:	Hunstanton Golf Club welcomes visitors without restriction by arrangement with the Secretary – Contact Tel. 0485 532811.
Ladies & Juniors:	As for men.
Parties:	Parties are welcome by arrangement with the Secretary – Contact Tel. 0485 532811.
Green Fees:	Men & Ladies £28.00 per day (weekdays). Juniors half adult rate.
Club Hire:	Clubs are available for hire from the Professional's shop.
Caddies:	Caddies are not available. Caddy cars and a limited number of buggies are available for hire.
Practice Ground:	The club has a full length practice ground.
Catering:	Full catering facilities are available by arrangement with the Secretary.
Tee Times:	By arrangement with the Secretary – Tel. 0485 532811.
Handicap:	A handicap certificate is required.
Handicap Limit:	Men 28; Ladies 36; Juniors – Boys 28; Girls 36.

ILKLEY GOLF CLUB
(ESTABLISHED 1890)
Myddleton, Ilkley, LS29 0BE

Set in picturesque surroundings the Ilkley Golf Club has a charming parkland layout and extends a warm Yorkshire welcome to visitors. The course is not long but very challenging with a premium on accuracy. The river winds its way through the course and comes into play on several holes. It is one of England's oldest clubs having celebrated its centenary in 1990 and is justifiably proud of its long traditions.

Secretary:	Mr. G. Hirst Tel. 600214
Professional:	John Hammond
	Tel. 607463
Holes:	18
Length:	6262 yards.
	Par: 69 SSS: 70
Visitors:	Ilkley Golf Club welcomes visitors without restrictions. Jackets and ties must be worn in the clubhouse.
Ladies & Juniors:	Ladies as for men. Juniors must be accompanied by an adult.
Parties:	Parties are welcome by arrangement with the Secretary – Tel. 600214.
Green Fees:	Men & Ladies £25 per day; £32 per day at weekends. Juniors half the adult green fee.
Club Hire:	Club hire can be arranged.
Caddies:	There are no caddies available. Caddy cars and electric trolleys are available for hire. Buggies are not permitted.
Practice Ground:	The Club has a first class practice ground.
Catering:	The Clubhouse offers full catering facilities.
Tee Times:	Contact the Professional – Tel. 607463.
Handicap:	An official handicap certificate is required.
Handicap Limit:	Men 28; Ladies 36; Juniors 23.

KETTERING GOLF CLUB
(ESTABLISHED 1891)
The Headlands, Kettering, Northants, NN15 6XA

Kettering was the pioneering club for golf in Northamptonshire. The original nine-hole course was laid out by Old Tom Morris and when the course was extended to eighteen holes three years later an exhibition match was played to celebrate between J. H. Taylor, the then reigning Open Champion, and the champion of three years earlier, Hugh Kirkaldy. It is a course perfectly manageable for length, a great pleasure to play and a place where visitors will find the warmest of welcomes.

Secretary:	Mr J. P. B. Galt Tel. 0536 511104
Professional:	Kevin Theobald Tel. 0536 81014
Holes:	18
Length:	6035 yards.
	Par: 69 SSS: 69
Visitors:	The Club welcomes visitors on weekdays only.
Ladies & Juniors:	As for men.
Parties:	Parties are welcome on Wednesdays and Fridays only by arrangement with the Secretary – Tel. 0536 511104.
Green Fees:	Men & Ladies – £20 per day.
Club Hire:	Clubs are not available for hire.
Caddies:	Caddies are not available. Caddy cars are available for hire from the Professional's shop.
Practice Ground:	The Club has a full length practice ground.
Catering:	The Clubhouse offers full catering facilities.
Tee Times:	By arrangement with the Secretary – Tel. 0536 511104.
Handicap:	A handicap certificate is required.
Handicap Limit:	Men 28; Ladies 36; Juniors 28.

LINDRICK GOLF CLUB
THE SHEFFIELD AND
DISTRICT GOLF CLUB
(ESTABLISHED 1891)

Lindrick Common, Worksop, Nr. Sheffield, S81 8BH

Marvellous heathland turf awaits the visitor to the famous Lindrick Club in Yorkshire, scene of the last British victory in the Ryder Cup in 1953 before reinforcements from Europe were brought in to beat the Americans at The Belfry in 1985. Lindrick has been in the vanguard of the movement to preserve traditional British golfing turf and there are few better examples than this challenging course with its fine fairways and firm, fast greens all year round.

Secretary:	Mr Garry Bywater Tel. 0909 475282
Professional:	Peter Cowen Tel. 0909 475820
Holes:	18
Length:	6615 yards.
	Par: 71 SSS: 72
Visitors:	Visitors are welcome except on Tuesdays or at weekends from November to March.
Ladies & Juniors:	As for men.
Parties:	Parties are welcome by arrangement with the Secretary – Tel. 0909 475282.
Green Fees:	Men and Ladies £30 per day; Juniors half adult green fee.
Club Hire:	Clubs are not available for hire.
Caddies:	Caddies are available by arrangement. Caddie cars and electric trollies are available for hire.
Practice Ground:	The Club has a full length practice ground.
Catering:	The Clubhouse offers full catering facilities in the dining room. Collar and tie must be worn at all times.
Tee Times:	By arrangement with the Secretary – Tel. 0909 475282.
Handicap:	A handicap certificate is required.
Handicap Limit:	Men 28; Ladies 36.

LUFFENHAM HEATH GOLF CLUB
(ESTABLISHED 1911)
Ketton, Stamford, Lincs., PE9 3UU

This is heathland golf at its best and a course not so well known to the golfing public. It was a favourite of the Prince of Wales, a former Captain of the Club, before he became King Edward VIII. The course, laid out by James Braid, is set in pleasant rolling countryside and presents just enough of a challenge to make it interesting indeed. It is one of the gems of English golf.

Secretary:	Mr I. F. Davenport Tel. 0780 720205
Professional:	J. N. Lawrence Tel. 0780 720298
Holes:	18
Length:	6250 yards.
	Par: 70 SSS: 70
Visitors:	The Club welcomes visitors by arrangement with the Secretary – Tel. 0780 720205.
Ladies & Juniors:	As for men.
Parties:	Parties are welcome Wednesdays, Thursdays and Fridays only. Restricted to 36 players.
Green Fees:	Men & Ladies — Weekdays £28 per day; Weekends £34 per day; Juniors Weekdays £14; Weekends £17.
Club Hire:	Clubs are available for hire from the Professional's shop.
Caddies:	There are no caddies available. Caddy cars are available for hire.
Practice Ground:	The Club has a short practice ground.
Catering:	The Clubhouse offers full catering facilities on application to the Secretary.
Tee Times:	By arrangement with the Secretary or Professional – Tel. 0780 720205/720298.
Handicap:	A handicap certificate is required.
Handicap Limit:	Men 28; Ladies 36; Juniors 36.

MANOR HOUSE HOTEL
(ESTABLISHED 1921)
Moretonhampstead, Devon

Set in magnificent surroundings on the edge of Dartmoor, the Manor House Hotel offers not only gracious surroundings to its visitors but a golf course of great charm and beauty. Not long at just over 6000 yards it is still a stiff enough challenge and the late Sir Henry Cotton rated the long Par 4 7th hole, with its winding stream, one of his favourites anywhere. The course has hosted the West of England PGA Championship and visitors will find excellent facilities and a warm welcome.

Secretary/ Professional:	Mr Richard Lewis Tel. 0647 40355
Holes:	18
Length:	6016 yards.
	Par: 69 SSS: 69
Visitors:	There are no golf course restrictions for visitors.
Ladies & Juniors:	As for men.
Parties:	Parties are welcome by arrangement with the Secretary – Tel. 0647 40355.
Green Fees:	Mens & Ladies £20.50 per day, £25.50 at weekends. Juniors half adult green fee.
Club Hire:	Club hire can be arranged.
Caddies:	There are no caddies available. Caddy cars and buggies are available for hire.
Practice Ground:	The Club has a full length practice ground.
Catering:	The Clubhouse offers full catering facilities.
Tee Times:	Contact the Secretary – Tel. 0647 40355.
Handicap:	An official handicap certificate is required.
Handicap Limit:	Men 28; Ladies 36; Juniors 36.

The Manor House Hotel

MOORTOWN GOLF CLUB
(FOUNDED 1909)
Harrogate Road, Alwoodley, Leeds LS17 7DB

Changes have been made in recent times to Dr Alister Mackenzie's original layout at Moortown. This fine moorland course has hosted the Ryder Cup and many important national events. It is also famous for the incident in the 1974 Brabazon Trophy when Nigel Denham overclubbed at the last hole and found his ball in the clubhouse bar. He then chipped through an open window back on to the green

Secretary:	Mr R. H. Brown Tel. 0532 686521
Professional:	Bryon Hutchinson Tel. 0532 683636
Holes:	18
Length:	7020 yards.
	Par: 71 SSS: 74
Visitors:	Visitors are welcome without restriction.
Ladies & Juniors:	As for Men.
Parties:	Parties are not allowed on Mondays but on all other days by arrangement with the Secretary – Tel. 0532 686521.
Green Fees:	£30 per round; £35 per day all categories.
Club Hire:	Clubs are not available for hire.
Caddies:	Caddies are available by arrangement. Caddie cars and electric trollies are available for hire.
Practice Ground:	The Club has a full length practice ground.
Catering:	The Club has full catering facilities. Contact the Catering Manager – Tel. 0532 688746.
Tee Times:	Contact the Secretary – Tel. 0532 686521 or the Professional – Tel. 0532 683636.
Handicap:	A handicap certificate is required.
Handicap Limit:	National handicap limits apply.

OLD THORNS
(ESTABLISHED 1982)
Old Thorns, Longmoor Road, Liphook, Hampshire, GU30 7PE

The Old Thorns club is part of a modern hotel and leisure complex owned by the London Kosaido Co Ltd. It was originally the brainchild of businessman Ken Wood who wanted to build his own private golf course. Commander John Harris drew up the first plans but died before they could be implemented. Peter Alliss and Dave Thomas completed the work and produce a fine course in rolling Hampshire countryside.

General Manager:	Mr G. M. Jones Tel. 0428 724555
Professional:	Phil Loxley Tel. 0428 724555
Holes:	18
Length:	6529 yards.
	Par: 72 SSS: 71
Visitors:	Old Thorns welcomes visitors without restrictions.
Ladies & Juniors:	As for men.
Parties:	Parties are welcome by prior arrangement with the Manager – Tel. 0428 724555.
Green Fees:	£22 per round, £35 per day midweek. Weekends and bank holidays £32 per round. Special rates are available for parties and large groups.
Club Hire:	Club hire can be arranged.
Caddies:	There are no caddies available. Caddy cars are available from the Professional's shop.
Practice Ground:	The Club has practice facilities.
Catering:	The Clubhouse and hotel provide full catering facilities without restrictions.
Tee Times:	Contact the General Manager – Tel. 0428 724555.
Handicap:	Not required.
Handicap Limit:	None.

PRINCE'S GOLF CLUB
(FOUNDED 1905)
Sandwich Bay, Sandwich, Kent, CT13 9QB

There have been many changes at Prince's since Gene Sarazen won the Open Championship there with a record total in 1932. The original course became a victim of the Second World War when it was torn up for the more immediate needs of military training. A new layout of three nine hole loops was rebuilt and in recent times a new clubhouse has been built. Prince's is a particularly friendly club offering a very warm welcome to visitors.

Secretary:	Visitors enquiries to Mr G. Ramm Tel. 0304 611118
Professional:	Philip Sparks Tel. 0304 613797
Holes:	27
Length:	18 – 6690 or 6510 or 6506 dependent on combination of three nine hole layouts. Par: 72, 71; 71 SSS: 72; 71; 71
Visitors:	The Club is very happy to welcome visitors. Restrictions only for major events.
Ladies & Juniors:	Ladies and Juniors are particularly welcome.
Parties:	Parties are welcome by arrangement with G. Ramm J. H. Adams – Tel. 0304 611118.
Green Fees:	Men and Ladies: Weekdays £26.50 per round, £29 per day; Sat and Bank Hols. £31 per round, £34 per day; Sundays £31 per round, £39 per day. Juniors: reduced green fee.
Club Hire:	Clubs are available for hire from the Professional's shop.
Caddies:	Caddies are available by arrangement. Caddy cars are available for hire.
Practice Ground:	The Club has practice facilities.
Catering:	The Clubhouse offers full catering facilities by arrangement.
Tee Times:	Contact G. Ramm J. Adams Tel. 0304 613797.
Handicap:	A handicap certificate is required.
Handicap Limit:	Men 28; Ladies 36.

REIGATE HEATH GOLF CLUB
(FOUNDED 1895)
Reigate Heath, Reigate, Surrey, RH2 8QR

Built around a hill on top of which stands the clubhouse and an old windmill, Reigate Heath is one of those fine nine hole courses – and there are several around the country – which are an absolute joy to play. Set among heather and gorse this is traditional heathland with marvellous views towards Dorking and to Leith Hill and Ranmore Common. It is well worth a visit.

Secretary:	Mrs D.M. Howard Tel. 0737 245530
Professional:	Harry Carter
Holes:	9
Length:	5554 yards.
	Par: 67 SSS: 67
Visitors:	The Club welcomes visitors except at weekends.
Ladies & Juniors:	As for men.
Parties:	Parties are welcome on Wednesdays and Thursdays only by arrangement with the Secretary – Tel. 0737 245530.
Green Fees:	Men & Ladies £18 per round; £24 per day. Juniors £5 per round £8 per day with member only.
Club Hire:	Clubs are not available for hire.
Caddies:	There are no caddies available. Caddy cars are available for hire.
Practice Ground:	The Club has a short practice ground.
Catering:	The Clubhouse offers full catering facilities except on Mondays. Contact the Steward – Tel. 0737 242610.
Tee Times:	Contact the Secretary – Tel. 0737 245530 or the Steward – Tel. 0737 242610.
Handicap:	A handicap certificate is required.
Handicap Limit:	There is no handicap limit.

Royal Birkdale, the clubhouse and 18th hole

ROYAL BIRKDALE GOLF CLUB
(FOUNDED 1889)
Waterloo Road, Birkdale, Southport PR8 2LX

Since 1946 hardly a year has gone by without Royal Birkdale hosting a major golf event. Although the course did not come into prominence as a championship venue until relatively recent times, it has a long history and celebrated its centenary in 1989. The start of the Second World War prevented the 1940 Open from being staged there but it was played at Birkdale for the first time in 1954. In 1991 Ian Baker-Finch became the sixth Open Champion to be crowned on this famous Southport links.

Secretary:	Mr. Norman Crewe Tel. 0704 67920.
Professional:	Richard Bradbeer Tel. 0704 68857
Holes:	18
Length:	6703 yards
	Par: 72 SSS: 73
Visitors:	Royal Birkdale welcomes visitors without restriction.
Ladies & Juniors:	As for men.
Parties:	Parties are welcome except at weekends and subject to certain midweek restrictions. Contact the Secretary Tel. 0704 67920.
Green Fees:	Men, Ladies and Juniors £46 per round, £67 per day. Weekly rates are not available.
Club Hire:	Clubs are available for hire from the professionals.
Caddies:	Caddies are available by arrangement.
Practice Ground:	The Club has a full length practice ground.
Catering:	The Club offers full catering facilities but there are restrictions in the dining room on parties of 20 and over.
Tee Times:	Contact the Secretary Tel. 0704 67920.
Handicap:	A handicap certificate is required.
Handicap Limit:	There is no handicap limit.

The Royal Cinque Ports Golf Club

THE ROYAL CINQUE PORTS GOLF CLUB
(FOUNDED 1892)
Golf Road, Deal, Kent, CT14 6RF

The great golf writer Bernard Darwin rated the classic links of Deal at the very top of his list of challenging courses. This famous course on that marvellous stretch of golfing country on the Kent coast has been the venue for the Open Championship twice. It is also the home base of the Halford Hewitt Cup played every April between the public schools golfing societies.

Secretary	Clive W. Greaves Tel. 0304 374007
Professional:	Andrew Reynolds Tel. 0304 374170
Holes:	18
Length:	6407 yards. Par: 70 SSS: 71
Visitors:	The Club welcomes visitors by arrangement with the Secretary, normally Mondays, Tuesdays and Thursdays after 9.30 am.
Ladies & Juniors:	Ladies as for men. Juniors by prior arrangement with the Secretary.
Parties:	Parties are welcome at certain times of year by prior arrangement with the Secretary.
Green Fees:	Men and Ladies – £25 per round; £35 per day weekdays only. Juniors under 16 £12.50 per round; £17.50 per day.
Club Hire:	Clubs are available for hire.
Caddies:	Caddies are available by arrangement. Caddy cars and electric trollies are available for hire. The Club has one buggy for hire.
Practice Ground:	The Club has a full length practice ground.
Catering:	The Clubhouse offers full catering facilities subject to prior arrangement.
Tee Times:	By arrangement with the Secretary – Tel. 0304 374007.
Handicap:	A handicap certificate is required.
Handicap Limit:	Men 20; Ladies 24; Juniors by arrangement with the Secretary.

ROYAL LIVERPOOL GOLF CLUB
(FOUNDED 1869)
Meols Drive, Hoylake, Wirral, Merseyside

For decades the Royal Liverpool Club at Hoylake was recognised as the most important golf club in England. It is steeped in history, the Amateur Championship had its origins there and it lies only behind Westward Ho! in the antiquity of English courses. It was also the home of great amateur players like John Ball who won the Amateur Championship eight times and Harold Hilton, the first player to hold the amateur titles on both sides of the Atlantic in the same year.

Secretary:	Mr R. H. White Tel. 051 632 2101
Professional:	John Heggarty Tel. 051 632 5868
Holes:	18
Length:	7110 yards. Par: 74 SSS: 74
Visitors:	The Club welcomes visitors but not before 9.30 am or between 1–2 pm and only a limited number at weekends.
Ladies & Juniors:	As for men but not before midday at weekends.
Parties:	Parties are welcome by arrangement with the Secretary – Tel. 051 632 3101.
Green Fees:	Men £32 per round, £45 per day. Ladies £25 per round, £35 per day. Juniors as for Ladies.
Club Hire:	Clubs are available for hire.
Caddies:	Caddies are available by arrangement. Caddy cars and electric trollies are available for hire.
Practice Ground:	The Club has a full length practice ground.
Catering:	The Clubhouse offers full catering facilities. However, lunch and dinner is normally available only to parties of 20 or more.
Tee Times:	By arrangement with The Starter for four or less – Tel. 051 632 6757.
Handicap:	A handicap certificate is required.
Handicap Limit:	Men 28; Ladies 36; Juniors 28.

ROYAL LYTHAM AND ST ANNES
(FOUNDED 1886)
Links Gate, Lytham & St. Annes, Lancashire, FY8 3LQ

Bobby Jones won the first of his three Open Championships at Royal Lytham in 1926, the first time the Club played host to the event. Since then it has staged many memorable Opens none more historic than Tony Jacklin's memorable victory in 1969 when he became the first British winner for eighteen years. Although it is a links course it is unusual in being surrounded by houses.

Secretary:	Major A. S. Craven Tel. 0253 724206
Professional:	Eddie Birchenough Tel. 0253 720094
Holes:	18
Length:	6673 yards.
	Par: 72 SSS: 73
Visitors:	The Club welcomes visitors between the hours of 09.30 and 12.00 and 14.30 and 16.00 but not Tuesdays am or weekends.
Ladies & Juniors:	Ladies as for men. Juniors by arrangement and with suitable handicap.
Parties:	Parties are welcome by arrangement with the Secretary – Tel. 0253 724206. All players must have a handicap certificate from a recognised golf club.
Green Fees:	Men & Ladies £36 per round; £50 per day.
Club Hire:	Clubs are not available for hire.
Caddies:	There are no caddies available. Electric trollies are available for hire.
Practice Ground:	The Club has a full length practice ground.
Catering:	The Clubhouse offers full catering facilities.
Tee Times:	By arrangement with the Secretary – Tel. 0253 724206.
Handicap:	A handicap certificate is required. Society handicaps unless EGU accredited are not acceptable.
Handicap Limit:	Men 28; Ladies 36; Juniors by arrangement.

Royal Lytham and St Annes

ROYAL NORTH DEVON
GOLF CLUB
(FOUNDED 1864)
Golf Links Road, Westward Ho!, Bideford, Devon, EX39 1HD

The great seaside links at Westward Ho! are the oldest in England and in earlier days ranked second only in importance to Hoylake. Ponies and sheep still wander the course giving a flavour of earlier times. Pot bunkers and sea rushes, a fearsome vegetation which can impale a golf ball, are features of this historic course. It was at Westward Ho! that J. H. Taylor, five times winner of the Open Championship and the last survivor of the Great Triumvirate, learned to play. He died at nearby Northam in 1963.

Secretary:	Mr E. J. Davies Tel. 0237 473817
Professional:	G. Johnston Tel. 0237 477598
Holes:	18
Length:	6662 yards.
	Par: 72 SSS: 72
Visitors:	The Club welcomes visitors.
Ladies & Juniors:	As for men.
Parties:	Parties are welcome by arrangement.
Green Fees:	Men and Ladies £16 per round; £24 per day. Juniors £6 per round; £8 per day.
Club Hire:	Clubs are available for hire from the Professional's shop.
Caddies:	There are no caddies available. Caddy cars and electric trollies are available for hire.
Practice Ground:	The Club has a full length practice ground.
Catering:	The Clubhouse offers full catering facilities.
Tee Times:	By arrangement – Tel. 0237 423456.
Handicap:	A handicap certificate is required.
Handicap Limit:	There is no handicap limit.

THE ROYAL ST GEORGE'S GOLF CLUB
(FOUNDED 1887)
Sandwich, Kent, CT13 9PB

For the first 33 years of existence the Open Championship was strictly a Scottish preserve. But in 1894 the Royal and Ancient Golf Club, organisers of the event, decided it should be played in England for the first time and they gave the honour to the famous links of Royal St. George's at Sandwich. Since then it has been played there ten times with memorable victories by Henry Cotton in 1934 when he broke the American grip on the event and by Sandy Lyle in 1985.

Secretary:	Mr Gerald Watts Tel. 0304 613090
Professional:	Niall Cameron Tel. 0304 615236
Holes:	18
Length:	6534 yards.
	Par: 70 SSS: 74
Visitors:	The Club welcomes male visitors with a handicap of 18 or better with an introduction.
Ladies & Juniors:	Women 15 handicap and under are welcome but must play with a member. There is no provision for Juniors.
Parties:	Parties are welcome under the same restrictions as for guests.
Green Fees:	Men £33 per round; £47 per day.
Club Hire:	Clubs are available for hire from the Professional's shop.
Caddies:	Caddies are available by arrangement. Electric trollies are available for hire.
Practice Ground:	The Club has a full length practice ground.
Catering:	The Clubhouse offers full catering facilities.
Tee Times:	By arrangement with the Secretary – Tel. 0304 613090.
Handicap:	A handicap certificate is required.
Handicap Limit:	Men 18; Ladies 15.

ROYAL WEST NORFOLK GOLF CLUB
(FOUNDED 1892)
Brancaster, Nr. King's Lynn, Norfolk, PE31 8AX

In this remote corner of England time has stood almost still and golf is played as it was nearly a century ago when this historic club was founded. There are shades of the Victorians at play here and there are few more enjoyable places for lovers of the great traditions of the royal and ancient game. Beware the high tides for there are times when the club is cut off from civilisation but it is no hardship at all to be marooned at Brancaster.

Secretary:	Maj. N.A. Carrington Smith Tel. 0485 210087
Professional:	R.E. Kimber Tel. 0485 210616
Holes:	18
Length:	6428 yards. Par: 71 SSS: 71
Visitors:	Visitors are welcome by prior arrangement with the Secretary – Tel. 0485 210037 outwith July and August and 1st week in September.
Ladies & Juniors:	As for men.
Parties:	Parties are welcome by prior arrangement with the Secretary but limited to 24 in number.
Green Fees:	Men & Ladies £25 per round weekdays; £30 per round weekends. Juniors half green fee if under 16.
Club Hire:	Clubs are available for hire from the Professional's shop.
Caddies:	Caddies are available by arrangement with the Professional – Tel. 0485 210616. Caddy cars are available for hire. Buggies may be used by the disabled or infirm by prior arrangement with the Secretary.
Practice Ground:	The Club has a full length practice ground.
Catering:	The Clubhouse offers full catering facilities by arrangement with the Steward Tel. 0485 210223.
Tee Times:	By arrangement with the Secretary – Tel. 0485 210087.
Handicap:	A handicap certificate is required.
Handicap Limit:	There is no handicap limit.

ROYAL WORLINGTON & NEWMARKET GOLF CLUB
(ESTABLISHED 1893)
Links Road, Worlington, Bury St. Edmunds

Royal Worlington is universally regraded as the best nine-hole golf course in the world. Bernard Darwin thought so and so did Henry Longhurst, neither of whom could be regarded as bad judges. Built on sandy heathland it is the home course of Cambridge University and a joyous place to play. Luncheon at this historic club is legendary and as much a part of the visit as the excellent golf itself.

Secretary:	Mr. C. P. Simpson Tel. 0638 712216
Professional:	Mr. Malcolm Hawkins Tel. 0638 715224
Holes:	9
Length:	3105 yards
	Par: 35 SSS: 70
Visitors:	Royal Worlington & Newmarket Golf Club welcomes visitors Monday to Friday but at weekends only with a member.
Ladies & Juniors:	Ladies as for men. Juniors: Mondays to Fridays only if accompanied.
Parties:	Parties are welcome by arrangement with the Secretary – Tel. 0638 712216
Green Fees:	Men, Ladies & Juniors – £25 per day.
Club Hire:	Clubs are available for hire limited to two half sets only.
Caddies:	Caddies are available by prior arrangement only. Electric trolleys are available for hire.
Practice Ground:	The Club has a full length practice ground.
Catering:	The Clubhouse offers luncheon facilities by prior arrangement only. Evening meals are not available.
Tee Times:	Tee times are by arrangement with the Secretary – Tel. 0638 712216.
Handicap:	A handicap certificate or a letter of introduction is required.
Handicap Limit:	Men 28; Ladies 36.

RYE GOLF CLUB
(ESTABLISHED 1894)
Camber, Rye, East Sussex, TN31 7QS

Rye is the place to find traditional golf and it is all the better for that. This marvellous old links has the best fescue greens in the world. Foursomes is very much the game and a warm welcome awaits in the cosy clubhouse afterwards. Rye is always a great winter course and the Oxford and Cambridge Golfing Society play their annual match for the President's Putter there in January.

Secretary:	Mr. J. M. Bradley Tel. 0797 225241
Professional:	Mr. P. Marsh
	Tel. 0797 225218
Holes:	27
Length:	6310 yards.
	Par: 68 SSS: 71
Visitors:	The Rye Golf Club welcomes visitors by introduction only.
Ladies & Juniors:	As for men.
Parties:	The Club does not welcome parties.
Green Fees:	Men & Ladies £26 per round; £39 per day: Juniors half adult green fees.
Club Hire:	Clubs are not available for hire.
Caddies:	There are no caddies available. Caddy cars are available for hire.
Practice Ground:	The Club has a full length practice ground.
Catering:	The Clubhouse caters for lunches only.
Tee Times:	Contact the Secretary – Tel. 0797 225241.
Handicap:	A handicap certificate is required.
Handicap Limit:	Men 18; Ladies 24; Juniors 24.

ST ENODOC GOLF CLUB
(ESTABLISHED 1891)
Rock, Wadeeridge, Cornwall, PL27 6LB,

There are wonderful views of the Camel Estuary looking across to Padstow and out to sea on this fine links on the northern edge of Cornwall. The giant "Himalayas" bunker at the 6th is a notable feature and should be avoided at all costs. The late Poet Laureate, Sir John Betjeman, is buried in the church which stands in the middle of this delightful course.

Secretary:	Mr. L. Guy Tel. 0208 86 3216
Professional:	Nick Williams
	Tel. 0208 86 2402
Holes:	Church Course 18
	Holywell Course 18
Length:	Church Course 6207
	Par: 69 SSS: 70
	Holywell Course 4165
	Par: 62 SSS: 61
Visitors:	The St Enodoc Golf Club welcomes visitors subject to handicap restrictions.
Ladies & Juniors:	As for men.
Parties:	Parties are welcome but on Saturdays are restricted to 20. Contact the Secretary – Tel. 0208 86 3216
Green Fees:	Church Course: Men & Ladies £20 per round; £30 per day; £112 per week. Holywell Course: Men & Ladies £12 per round; £18 per day; £56 per week. Juniors half the adult green fee.
Club Hire:	Club hire can be arranged.
Caddies:	Caddies are not available. Caddy cars are available for hire.
Practice Ground:	The Club has a practice ground.
Catering:	The Clubhouse offers full catering facilities.
Tee Times:	Contact the Secretary – Tel. 0208 86 3216.
Handicap:	A handicap certificate is required.
Handicap Limit:	Men 24; Ladies 28; Juniors 28.

ST MELLION
GOLF & COUNTRY CLUB
(ESTABLISHED 1976)
St. Mellion, Saltash, Cornwall, PL12 6SD

The vision and tenacity of brothers Martin and Hermon Bond was finally rewarded when their dream of building a truly championship course at St. Mellion was finally realised in 1987. They brought in Jack Nicklaus to design their dream course which was built alongside the Old Course established in 1976. The course that Jack built is no place for the faint of heart but it is a marvellous experience. St. Mellion was host to the Benson and Hedges International in 1990 and 1991.

Director:	Mr. David Webb Tel. 0579 50101
Professional:	Tony Moore Tel. 0579 50724
Holes:	36
Length:	Nicklaus 6626 yards. Par: 72 SSS: 72
	Old 5760 yards. Par: 69 SSS: 67
Visitors:	St Mellion Golf & Country Club welcomes visitors with an official handicap certificate only.
Ladies & Juniors:	As for men.
Parties:	Parties possessing official handicap certificates are welcome by arrangement with Mrs Penny Baxter Tel. 0579 50101.
Green Fees:	Nicklaus Course: Men and Ladies £50 per round; Juniors £25 per round. Group Business rate £40 per round. Old Course £17 per round.
Club Hire:	Club hire can be arranged.
Caddies:	Caddies are available by arrangement. Caddy cars, electric trollies and buggies are available for hire.
Practice Ground:	The Club has a full length practice ground.
Catering:	The Clubhouse offers full catering facilities in both restaurant and a grill room.
Tee Times:	Contact the Starters Office – Tel. 0579 51182.
Handicap:	An official handicap certificate is required.
Handicap Limit:	Men 28; Ladies 36; Juniors official handicap.

St Mellion Golf & Country Club

SAUNTON GOLF CLUB
(ESTABLISHED 1897)
Nr. Braunton, North Devon, EX33 1LG

Saunton is part of the biggest dune system in Europe and there are two fine courses to choose from on this classic links. The greens are outstanding for their quality and among the best in the country and the fairways are a joy to play from. Perhaps only the Old Course at St. Andrews has anything to equal the undulations of the putting surfaces. A warm welcome awaits the visitor but it is a busy club and advisable to make advance arrangements.

Secretary:	Mr. W. E. Geddes Tel. 0271 812436
Professional:	J. McGhee Tel. 0271 812013
Holes:	36
Length:	West Course 6356 yards.
	Par: 71 SSS: 71
	East Course 6703 yards.
	Par: 71 SSS: 73
Visitors:	Saunton Golf Club welcomes visitors who are members of recognised Golf Clubs.
Ladies & Juniors:	Ladies as for men. Juniors playing with an adult only.
Parties:	Parties are welcome by arrangement with the Secretary – Tel. 0271 812436
Green Fees:	£21.50 weekdays; £26.50 weekends for all players.
Club Hire:	Club hire is not available.
Caddies:	There are no caddies available. Caddy cars are avilable for hire.
Practice Ground:	The Club has a full length practice ground.
Catering:	The Clubhouse offers full catering facilities.
Tee Times:	Contact the Secretary – Tel. 0271 812436.
Handicap:	A handicap certificate is required.
Handicap Limit:	There is no handicap limit.

SEATON CAREW GOLF CLUB
(ESTABLISHED 1874)
Tee Road, Seaton Carew, Hartlepool, Cleveland, TS25 1DE

Just north of Middlesborough lies an old and respected links which has survived the march of time and although it is overlooked by giant chemical plants it matters not for Seaton Carew is a delightful place to play golf. It is one of England's oldest courses and is a lovely haven amidst so much industry. It is a fine test by any standards with good crisp links turf and fine greens to putt on.

Secretary:	Mr. T. Waite Tel. 0429 267645
Professional:	Mr. William Hector
	Tel. 0429 266249
Holes:	22 (in combination)
Length:	The Old Course 6604 yards.
	Par: 72
	The Brabazon Course 6849 yards.
	Par: 73
Visitors:	Seaton Carew Golf Club welcomes visitors by arrangement with the Secretary – Tel: 0429 267645.
Ladies & Juniors:	As for men.
Parties:	Parties are welcome by prior arrangement with the Secretary.
Green Fees:	Old Course: Men & Ladies £18 per day: Juniors £11 per day. Brabazon Course: Men & Ladies £25 per day; Juniors £11 per day.
Club Hire:	Clubs are available for hire.
Caddies:	Caddies are available by arrangement. Caddy cars are available for hire.
Practice Ground:	The Club has a practice ground.
Catering:	The Clubhouse offers full catering facilities by prior arrangement only. Contact Mr C. Hartley – Tel. 0429 261040.
Tee Times:	Contact the Secretary – Tel. 0429 267645.
Handicap:	An official handicap certificate is required.
Handicap Limit:	There is no handicap limit.

SILLOTH ON SOLWAY GOLF CLUB
(ESTABLISHED 1892)
The Clubhouse, Silloth, Carlisle, Cumbria, CA5 4BL

Just south of the Scottish border lies another of England's finest links courses. Silloth is famous for its Cumberland, sea-washed turf and this fine links course is well provided with it. The great lady golfer, Cecil Leitch, played out of Silloth on Solway and brought great credit to her Club in a distinguished career. The views across the Solway Firth towards Scotland are a memorable part of any visit to this great course.

Secretary:	Mr. G. A. Doughty Tel. 0697 31304
Professional:	John Burns
	Tel. 0697 31304
Holes:	18
Length:	6357 yards.
	Par: 72 SSS: 71
Visitors:	Silloth on Solway Golf Club welcomes visitors except at weekends and on Bank Holidays.
Ladies & Juniors:	As for men.
Parties:	Parties are welcome by arrangement with Mrs. N. Burns – Tel. 0697 31304 except Mondays, Fridays and weekends. Maximum number 40
Green Fees:	Men & Ladies — weekdays £15 per round; Weekends and Bank Holidays £21 per round; £65 per week. Juniors half adult green fee.
Club Hire:	Clubs are not available for hire.
Caddies:	There are no caddies available. Caddy cars are available for hire.
Practice Ground:	The Club has a full length practice ground.
Catering:	The Clubhouse offers full catering facilities except on Mondays.
Tee Times:	Contact the Professional – Tel. 0697 31304.
Handicap:	A official handicap certificate is required.
Handicap Limit:	There is no handicap limit.

Silloth on Solway golf course

SUNNINGDALE GOLF CLUB
(ESTABLISHED 1900)
Ridgemount Road, Sunningdale, Ascot, Berkshire, SL5 9RR

The famous Old Course at Sunningdale is a wonderful heathland layout rightly regarded as the finest inland course in the country. It is not too demanding but it is as delightful a place to play as can be found anywhere. It was here that Bobby Jones had his famous "perfect round" of 66 with 33 for each half and 33 each of shots and putts in the Open Championship qualifying rounds in 1926. The New Course, designed by Harry Colt, is in many critics' eyes a tougher test than that set by Willie Park.

Secretary:	Mr. Stewart Zuill Tel. 0344 21681
Professional:	Keith Maxwell Tel. 0344 20128
Holes:	36
Length:	Old Course – 6586 yards.
	Par: 72 SSS: 71
	New Course – 6676 yards.
	Par: 70 SSS: 72
Visitors:	Sunningdale Golf Club welcomes visitors by prior arrangement only. Visitors must be members of recognised Golf Clubs and be in possession of an official handicap.
Ladies & Juniors:	Ladies: As for men but Mondays to Fridays only. There is no usual provision for Juniors.
Parties:	Parties are welcome by prior arrangement with the Secretary – Tel. 0344 21681.
Green Fees:	Men & Ladies £70 per day.
Club Hire:	Clubs hire can be arranged.
Caddies:	Caddies are available. Caddy cars can be hired from the Professional's shop.
Practice Ground:	The Club has practice facilities.
Catering:	The Clubhouse offers full catering facilities except on Mondays.
Tee Times:	Contact the Secretary – Tel. 0344 21681.
Handicap:	An official handicap certificate is required.
Handicap Limit:	Men 18; Ladies 24.

TADMARTON HEATH GOLF CLUB
(ESTABLISHED 1922)
Wigginton, Bambury, Oxon, OX15 5HL

This excellent course situated five miles from Bambury in North Oxfordshire is another of England's fine examples of heathland golf. Roger Wethered enjoyed the course with its gorse-lined fairways and played there regularly. There are also some marvellous Cotswold views to enhance the challenge which is not long by some standards but much more enjoyable than most.

Secretary:	Mr. R. E. Wackrill Tel. 0608 737649
Professional:	Les Bond Tel. 0608 730047
Holes:	18
Length:	5917 yards.
	Par: 69 SSS: 69
Visitors:	Tadmarton Heath Golf Club welcomes visitors who are members of recognised Golf Clubs on weekdays only.
Ladies & Juniors:	As for men or with a member.
Parties:	Parties are welcome up to a maximum of 36 players by arrangement with the Secretary – Tel. 0608 737649.
Green Fees:	Men and Ladies £25 per day. Juniors £12 per day.
Club Hire:	Club hire can be arranged.
Caddies:	There are no caddies available. Electric trolleys are available for hire.
Practice Ground:	The Club has a short practice ground.
Catering:	The Clubhouse offers full catering facilities.
Tee Times:	Contact the Secretary – Tel. 0608 737278.
Handicap:	A official handicap certificate is required.
Handicap Limit:	There is no handicap limit.

THORPENESS GOLF CLUB
(ESTABLISHED 1925)
Thorpeness, Leiston, Suffolk, 1P16 4NH

Situated a hundred miles from London on the tranquil Suffolk coast Thorpeness is a charming heathland course set among gorse and heather with spinneys of silver birch. Not overly long it nevertheless presents a first class challenge for any level of ability. James Braid laid out the course in 1925 and there are some marvellous views including that of the nearby Windmill and the House in the Clouds, an unusual house built on a pedestal.

Secretary:	Mr. N. W. Griffin Tel. 0728 45 2176
Professional:	Tony Pennock
	Tel. 0728 45 2524
Holes:	18
Length:	6241 yards.
	Par: 69 SSS: 71
Visitors:	Thorpeness Golf Club welcomes visitors without restriction.
Ladies & Juniors:	As for men.
Parties:	Parties are welcome.
Green Fees:	Men & Ladies £20.50 per round; £31 per day: Juniors half adult green fee.
Club Hire:	Club hire can be arranged.
Caddies:	Caddies are available by arrangement. Caddy cars, electric trollies and buggies are available.
Practice Ground:	The Club has a full length practice ground.
Catering:	The Clubhouse offers full catering facilities.
Tee Times:	Contact the Professional – Tel. 0728 45 2524 or the Secretary 0728 45 2176.
Handicap:	An official handicap certificate is required.
Handicap Limit:	Men 28; Ladies 36; Juniors 36.

WALTON HEATH GOLF CLUB
(ESTABLISHED 1904)
Deans Lane, Tadworth, Surrey, KT20 7TP

Walton Heath lies high up on the North Downs and ranks among the toughest of British inland courses. It is a classic open heath course and the Club takes good care that it remains that way. The Club has two excellent courses which were laid out by Herbert Fowler. A combination layout from the two courses is used for championship events.

Secretary:	Mr. Norman G. Dampsey Tel. 0737 812380
Professional:	Ken MacPherson Tel. 0737 812152
Holes:	36
Length:	Old 6883 yards.
	Par: 73 SSS: 73
	New 6659 yards.
	par: 72 SSS: 72
Visitors:	Visitors are welcome at Walton Heath by prior arrangement only but not at weekends or on public holidays.
Ladies & Juniors:	As for men.
Parties:	Parties are welcome except at weekends or on public holidays by arrangement with the Assistant Secretary – Tel. 0737 812380.
Green Fees:	Men and Ladies £50 per day; £42 after 11.30 am. Juniors half the adult green fee.
Club Hire:	Clubs are available for hire.
Caddies:	Caddies are available. There are no caddy cars, electric trollies or buggies available.
Practice Ground:	The Club has a full length practice ground.
Catering:	The Clubhouse offers full catering facilities except for evening meals.
Tee Times:	Contact Mrs Janice Owen, Assistant Secretary – Tel. 0737 812380.
Handicap:	An official handicap certificate is required.
Handicap Limit:	Men 28; Ladies 36; Juniors as adults.

Walton Heath, the new course's 14th hole

WHITTINGTON BARRACKS GOLF CLUB
(ESTABLISHED 1886)
Tamworth Road, Lichfield

Whittington Barracks is another of England's fine heathland courses which can be savoured all the year round. Good turf and fine greens are the hallmark of this enjoyable course which lies just to the north of Birmingham. It is not overly long at 6457 yards but the par of 70 is a stiff test indeed for anyone. The course is another of England's oldest layouts and it is well worth a visit.

Administrator:	Mr. Nevil A. Spence Tel. 0543 432317
Professional:	Adrian Sadler Tel. 0543 432261
Holes:	18
Length:	6457 yards.
	Par: 70 SSS: 69
Visitors:	Whittington Barracks Golf Club welcomes visitors except at weekends.
Ladies & Juniors:	As for men.
Parties:	Parties are welcome on Wednesdays and Thursdays by arrangement with the Administrator – Tel: 0543 432317.
Green Fees:	£25 per day.
Club Hire:	Club hire can be arranged.
Caddies:	There are no caddies available. Caddy cars are available for hire from the Professional's shop.
Practice Ground:	The Club has a full length practice ground.
Catering:	The Clubhouse offers full catering facilities except on Mondays.
Tee Times:	Contact the Professional – Tel. 0543 432261.
Handicap:	An official handicap certificate is required.
Handicap Limit:	There is no handicap limit.

WALES

Despite its relatively small area compared to its immediate neighbours Wales is remarkably well supplied with golf courses. Somewhere over 120 in a recent count.

Although they were marginally beaten by Scotland and Ireland the Welsh were not slow to get to grips with championship golf and the Welsh Amateur Championship predates the English equivalent by a surprising thirty years.

It is a country not blessed with as many great links courses as its Gaelic cousins to the north and west, although the majestic links at Harlech and Royal Porthcawl are classic exceptions. However, there are many courses of great charm for the visitor to play.

Aberdovey is rightly famous and for more reason – although it is reason enough – than that the master writer on matters royal and ancient, Bernard Darwin, is on record as naming it "the course that my soul loves best of all the courses in the world".

It was at Aberdovey that he learned to play and he recalls in "Historic Golf Courses of the British Isles" the very beginnings of golf there in the early 1980's.

He recounts that the founder was Colonel Ruck "who, having played some golf at Formby, borrowed nine flower pots from a lady in the village and cut nine holes on the marsh to put them in".

Golf at Aberdovey and in Wales has come a long way since then.

ABERDOVEY GOLF CLUB
(ESTABLISHED 1892)
Aberdovey, Gwynedd, LL35 0RS

Famous as the course on which the legendary golf writer, Bernard Darwin, played as a boy and which he rated as ''the course that my soul loves best of all the courses in the world.'' It was laid out by his uncle and he won his first medal competition there in 1893. The club is renowned for its hospitality and many golf societies and Midlands golf clubs have made annual pilgrimages over many years. Masters Champion Ian Woosnam is another devotee and the course is renowned for the quality of its greens all year round

Secretary:	Mr. John M. Griffiths
Professional:	John Davies
	Tel. 0654 767 602
Holes:	18
Length:	6445 yards.
	Par: 71 SSS: 71
Visitors:	Aberdovey Golf Club welcomes visitors who are club members or have a handicap certificate.
Ladies & Juniors:	There are no restrictions on Ladies or Juniors.
Parties:	Parties are welcome by arrangement with the Secretary after 10 am but not between the hours of 12.30 and 2 pm.
Green Fees:	Men & Ladies £16.50 – £18.50 per round; £25 per day: Juniors £10 per round/per day. No weekly terms.
Club Hire:	No club hire is available.
Caddies:	Available on an irregular basis.
Practice Ground:	The Club has a short practice ground.
Catering:	Full catering facilities are available.
Tee Times:	Tee times can be arranged by contacting Mrs. M. T. Chilton – Tel. 0654 767.
Handicap:	A handicap certificate is required.
Handicap Limit:	Handicap limits are – Men 28; Ladies 36; Juniors 36.

ROYAL PORTHCAWL GOLF CLUB
(ESTABLISHED 1891)
Rest Bay, Porthcawl, Mid Glamorgan, CF36 3UW

There is not a single hole on the fine links of Royal Porthcawl which does not have a view of the sea. But it is not all seaside golf for part of the course climbs to the top of a hill where the fairways have more of a heathland feel about them. Heather and gorse are there in abundance to concentrate the mind but the course itself is not overly long from the normal tees at just over 6400 yards. From the back tees at close to 6700 yards it is a different proposition entirely and it has proved a great test for several memorable Amateur Championships.

Secretary:	Mr. A. W. Woolcott Tel. 0656 71 2251
Professional:	Graham Poor Tel. 0656 71 6984
Holes:	18
Length:	6691 yards. Par: 72 SSS: 74
Visitors:	The Club welcomes visitors on weekdays only. Members and Guests only at weekends. All players must have handicap certificates.
Ladies & Juniors:	As for men.
Parties:	Parties are welcome by arrangement.
Green Fees:	Men & Ladies £30 per day. Juniors £15 per day.
Club Hire:	Clubs are available for hire.
Caddies:	Caddies are not generally available but are available by arrangement occasionally during school holidays. There are no caddy cars or electric trollies available for hire.
Practice Ground:	The Club has a full length practice ground.
Catering:	The Clubhouse offers full catering facilities.
Tee Times:	By arrangement with the Secretary – Tel. 0656 71 2251.
Handicap:	A full handicap certificate is required.
Handicap Limit:	There is no handicap limit.

Royal Porthcawl golf course

ROYAL ST DAVID'S GOLF CLUB
(ESTABLISHED 1894)
Harlech, Gwynedd, LL46 2UB

Although laid out among the sandhills at Harlech the dunes do not really come into play until the end of the round and the course is quite flat. It is, however, a very fine test and has been host to the Mens' and Ladies' Home Internationals as well as the Ladies' British Open (Amateur). At its fullest stretch it measures under 6500 yards but as with all links courses the wind is the dominating factor. There are fine views of Snowdonia and the castle.

Secretary:	Mr. R. I. Jones Tel. 0766 780361
Professional:	John Barnett Tel. 0766 780857
Holes:	18
Length:	6427 yards. Par: 71 SSS: 69
Visitors:	The Club welcomes visitors by prior arrangement with the Secretary – Tel: 0766 780361.
Ladies & Juniors:	As for men.
Parties:	Visitors are welcome by prior arrangement with the Secretary or Professional – Tel. 0766 780857.
Green Fees:	Men & Ladies £20 per day weekdays; £25 per day weekends: £80 per week. Juniors half adult green fee.
Club Hire:	Clubs are not available for hire.
Caddies:	Caddies are not available except during school holidays. Caddy cars and electric trollies are available for hire. The Club has three buggies also available for hire.
Practice Ground:	The Club has practice facilities.
Catering:	The Clubhouse offers catering facilities but with a restricted service in the winter.
Tee Times:	By arrangement with the Secretary or Professional – Tel. 0766 780857.
Handicap:	A handicap certificate is required.
Handicap Limit:	Men 24; Ladies 28; Juniors 24.

SOUTHERNDOWN GOLF CLUB
(ESTABLISHED 1904)
Ewenny, Bridgend, Mid Glamorgan, CF31 4NF

Set high up on Ogmore Down visitors to the long established course at Southerndown will be met by marvellous views across the Bristol Channel to Devon and Cornwall. It is a tough challenge in the prevailing wind and there is a distinctly links feel about the course despite its elevation. The present layout is the work of architect Harry S. Colt and features fairways which are undulating and bordered by gorse and bracken. Visitors will find a warm Welsh welcome here.

Secretary:	Mr. R. Brickell Tel. 0656 880476
Professional:	D. McMonagle Tel. 0656 880326
Holes:	18
Length:	6613 yards.
	Par: 70 SSS: 73
Visitors:	Southerndown Golf Club welcomes visitors but with members only at weekends.
Ladies & Juniors:	As for men.
Parties:	Parties are welcome by arrangement with the Secretary – Tel. 0656 880476. Official handicap certificates are required.
Green Fees:	Men & Ladies £25 per day; £100 per week.
Club Hire:	Clubs are not available for hire.
Caddies:	There are no caddies available. Caddy cars are not available for hire.
Practice Ground:	The Club has practice facilities.
Catering:	The Clubhouse offers full catering facilities. Jackets & ties must be worn after 7 pm.
Tee Times:	Contact the Secretary – Tel. 0656 880476.
Handicap:	An official handicap certificate is required.
Handicap Limit:	Men 28; Ladies 36; Juniors 36.

IRELAND

When it comes to having a good time with great golf thrown in there is nowhere on earth to equal Ireland. There is no place the travelling golfer will be made more welcome and the courses at his disposal many believe to be the best in the world.

Certainly for spectacular scenery and outstanding challenge there are none better and when it comes to analysing the drama of the golfing day in the 19th hole over a glass or two of stout the genuine welcome of the Irish is unsurpassed.

Ireland has going on for 300 courses from which to choose, a surprising number perhaps when compared with a little more than a hundred in excess of that in the whole of Scotland where the game was born.

Ireland is festooned with wonderful courses with marvellous sounding names. Portmarnock, Ballybunion, Lahinch, Rosses Point all have wonderful ring to them and they are rightly famous the world over. But there are many, many more lesser known which offer the visitor marvellous golf and that ever-present Irish sense of hospitality and fun.

Royal Belfast is the oldest club in Ireland having been founded in 1881 but Royal Dublin came along only a few years later and there are others of great antiquity too. Portmarnock, which four-times Open Champion Bobby Locke rated as one of the very greatest courses in the world and which many who know about these things would say is better still than that, dates back to 1894.

Although it lies only ten miles north of Dublin it is a remote spot and although there is road access to the course today, in the days when W. C. Pickeman and George Ross set about founding the club the only way there was by rowing a boat across the estuary from Sutton.

Today it is much easier to play golf in Ireland and it is an experience not to be missed.

BALLYBUNION GOLF CLUB
(ESTABLISHED 1893)
Ballybunion, County Kerry, Eire

The Old Course at Ballybunion is undoubtedly one of the great golf courses anywhere in the world. Tucked away in the deep south-west of Ireland it takes not a little effort and determination to get there but the rewards for persistance are worth all the effort. This is classic links among great sand hills set hard against the sea. The New Course, built by Robert Trent Jones, is a relatively recent companion to its famous sister.

Secretary:	Mr. Sean Walsh Tel. 0353 68 27611
Professional:	Ted Higgins Tel. 0353 68 27209
Holes:	36
Length:	Old Course 6542 yards. Par: 71 SSS: 73
	New Course 6378 yards. Par: 72 SSS: 73
Visitors:	Ballybunion Golf Club welcomes visitors but reservations must be made in advance.
Ladies & Juniors:	As for men.
Parties:	Parties are welcome by arrangement with the reservations office – Tel. 0353 68 27146.
Green Fees:	Old Course: Men & Ladies £30 per round £40 per day. New Course: Men & Ladies £20 per round £40 per day. Juniors under 18 half adult green fee.
Club Hire:	Clubs can be hired by prior arrangement.
Caddies:	Caddies are available by arrangement. Caddy cars are available for hire from the Professional's shop.
Practice Ground:	The Club does not have practice facilities.
Catering:	The Clubhouse offers full catering facilities by arrangement with the Catering Manageress. – Tel. 0353 68 27620.
Tee Times:	By arrangement at the Reservations Office – Tel. 0353 68 27146.
Handicap:	An official handicap certificate is required.
Handicap Limit:	Men 24; Ladies 36; Juniors 28.

Ballybunion golf course

KILLARNEY
GOLF AND FISHING CLUB
(ESTABLISHED 1893)
Mahoney's Point, Killarney, County Kerry, Eire

Two great coures in an incomparable setting around the shores of Lough Leane in the south-west corner of Ireland await visitors to the Killarney Golf and Fishing Club. This is spectacular parkland golf in the shadow of the Kerry mountains and one of the most beautiful places to play in the world. The club was chosen as the venue for the 1991 Carrolls Irish Open and will host the Curtis Cup in 1996.

Secretary:	Mr. Tom Prendergast Tel. 0353 64 31034
Professional:	Tony Coveney Tel. 0353 64 31615
Holes:	36
Length:	Mahoney's Point 6775 yards.
	Par: 72 SSS: 72
	Killeen 7059 yards. Par: 72 SSS: 72
Visitors:	Visitors are welcome subject to handicap restrictions.
Ladies & Juniors:	As for men.
Parties:	Parties are welcome by arrangement with the Secretary – Tel. 0353 64 31034
Green Fees:	Men & Ladies £20 per round; £32 per day weekdays. Weekends £20 per round. Juniors £10 per round £20 per day.
Club Hire:	Clubs are available for hire from the Professional's shop.
Caddies:	Caddies are available by arrangement. Caddy cars are available for hire.
Practice Ground:	The Club has a full length practice ground.
Catering:	The Clubhouse offers full catering facilities.
Tee Times:	By arrangement with the Secretary's Office – Tel. 0353 64 31034.
Handicap:	A handicap certificate is required.
Handicap Limit:	Men 28; Ladies 36. Juniors: Male 28; Female 36.

LAHINCH GOLF CLUB
(ESTABLISHED 1892)
Lahinch, C. Clare, Ireland

Old Tom Morris laid out the first course at Lahinch in 1892 making it one of the oldest courses in Ireland. It is a truly majestic links which the great architect, Alister Mackenzie, reworked from the original layout in 1928 shortly before he built Augusta National with Bobby Jones. The course has changed little since these alterations although it has been lengthened slightly and it remains one of the finest of all the world's true tests of links golf.

Secretary:	Mr. Alan Reardon Tel. 010 353 81003 Fax 010 353 65 81592
Professional:	Robert McCavery Tel. 010 353 65 81003
Holes:	18
Length:	6696 yards.
	Par: 72 SSS: 73
Visitors:	Lahinch wlecomes visitors without restriction.
Ladies & Juniors:	No restrictions.
Parties:	Parties are welcome by arrangement with the Secretary Tel. 010 353 65 81003.
Green Fees:	Men and Ladies £25 per day, £125 per week; Juniors £10 per day, £50 per week.
Club Hire:	Clubs are available for hire from the Professional's shop.
Caddies:	Caddies are available by arrangement.
Practice Ground:	Lahinch has a full length practice ground.
Catering:	The Clubhouse offers full catering facilities. Contact the caterer Tel 010 353 65 81003.
Tee Times:	Contact the Secretary Tel. 010 353 65 81003.
Handicap:	An official handicap certificate is required.
Handicap Limit:	Men 28; Ladies 36; Boys 28; Girls 36.

Lahinch golf course

PORTMARNOCK GOLF CLUB
(ESTABLISHED 1894)
Portmarnock, County Dublin, Eire

Played from the back tees at more than 7000 yards this is one of the toughest golf courses in the world. However from the normal tees and with a bit of firmness in the fairways to help the ball roll it is far less fearsome and enjoyable for any level of ability. Water surrounds the course on three sides and in its earliest days it was only reachable by ferry boat. Portmarnock has 27 holes which can be played in variations of nines.

Secretary:	Mr. W. Bornemann Tel. 010 35 323082
Professional:	Joey Purcell Tel. 010 35 325157
Holes:	27
Length:	(Champ.) 6488 metres.
	Par: 72 SSS: 75
Visitors:	The Club welcomes visitors subject to available tee times.
Ladies & Juniors:	Ladies are welcome except at weekends and on public holidays. Juniors must be over 12 years of age with Club Handicap.
Parties:	Parties are welcome by arrangement with the Secretary/Manager – Tel. 010 35 323082. No parties permitted on Wednesday, Thursdays, Weekends or Bank Holidays. Maximum number 60.
Green Fees:	Men £35 per day; Ladies £15 per day.
Club Hire:	Clubs are available for hire from the Professional's shop.
Caddies:	Caddies are available by arrangement. Caddy cars are available for hire.
Practice Ground:	The Club does not have a practice ground.
Catering:	The Clubhouse offers full catering facilities although it is advisable to pre-book for parties of 12 or over.
Tee Times:	Contact the Secretary/Manager – Tel. 010 35 323082.
Handicap:	A handicap certificate is required.
Handicap Limit:	Men 24; Ladies 36. Juniors 18.

ROYAL COUNTY DOWN
GOLF CLUB
(ESTABLISHED 1889)
Newcastle, County Down, BT33 0AN, N. Ireland

In a glorious setting in the shadow of the Mountains of Mourne lies the magnificent links of the Royal County Down Golf Club. Rated by many as one of the most difficult golf courses in the world it is nonetheless a serenely beautiful place to play golf. The views are as spectacular as the golf and when the weather is clear the mountains of the Isle of Man can be seen across the great spread of Dundrum Bay. It was here that Michael Bonallack won his historic third consecutive Amateur Championship.

Secretary:	Mr. P. E. Rolph Tel. 03967 23314
Professional:	E. T. Jones Tel. 03967 22419
Holes:	18
Length:	6968 yards.
	Par: 72 SSS: 73
Visitors:	The Club welcomes visitors except on Saturdays.
Ladies & Juniors:	Ladies as for men. Juniors over 16 only.
Parties:	Parties are welcome by arrangement with the Secretary – Tel. 03967 23314.
Green Fees:	Men & Ladies £30 per day weekdays: £35 per day weekends. Juniors £15 per day.
Club Hire:	Clubs are available for hire from the Professional's shop.
Caddies:	Caddies are available by arrangement. Caddy cars and electric trollies are available for hire.
Practice Ground:	The Club has a short practice ground.
Catering:	The Clubhouse offers full catering facilities except at weekends.
Tee Times:	Contact the Secretary – Tel. 03967 23314.
Handicap:	A handicap certificate is required.
Handicap Limit:	Men 28; Ladies 36; Juniors 28.

ROYAL PORTRUSH GOLF CLUB
(ESTABLISHED 1888)
Bushmills Road, Portrush, County Antrim, N. Ireland

Portrush was the venue for the only Open Championship ever to be played off the British mainland. In 1951 the colourful Max Faulkner manufactured a marvellous shot which he swerved round a tree at the last hole to win an Open in which only two rounds were recorded under 70. That is a measure of how challenging this Harry S. Colt inspired layout set in spectacular scenery in the very north of Ireland.

Secretary:	Miss W. I. Erskine Tel. 0265 822311
Professional:	Dai Stevenson Tel. 0265 823335
Holes:	18
Length:	6772 yards.
	Par: 72 SSS: 73
Visitors:	The Club welcomes visitors by prior arrangement with the Secretary – Tel. 0265 822311.
Ladies & Juniors:	Ladies as for men. Juniors may play with members only.
Parties:	Parties are welcome Mondays, Tuesdays & Thursdays, Wednesdays and Fridays pm only by arrangement with the Secretary – Tel. 0265 822311.
Green Fees:	Men & Ladies £25 per day weekdays; £30 per day weekends. Juniors as for adults.
Club Hire:	Clubs are available for hire from the Professional's shop.
Caddies:	Caddies are available by arrangement. Caddy cars and electric trollies are available for hire.
Practice Ground:	The Club has a full length practice ground.
Catering:	The Clubhouse offers full catering facilities.
Tee Times:	Contact the Secretary – Tel. 0265 822311.
Handicap:	A handicap certificate is required.
Handicap Limit:	There is no handicap limit.

INDEX